Maths Action Plans

Measures, Shape and Space

Y5/P6

David Clemson and Wendy Clemson

Published in 2002 by:
Nelson Thornes Ltd
Delta Place
27 Bath Road
CHELTENHAM
GL53 7TH
United Kingdom

02 03 04 05 06/ 10 9 8 7 6 5 4 3 2 1

A catalogue record for this book is available from the British Library

ISBN 0-7487-6319-8

Edited by Claire Watts
Illustrations by Tristram Ariss
Page make-up by Carla Turchini

Printed in Great Britain by Ashford Colour Press

Acknowledgements
The authors and publishers are grateful for permission to reproduce
copyright material as follows:
'Maths in chocolate making' screenshot © Cadbury Limited.
'Maths Explorer: Shape and Space' screenshot © Granada Learning Ltd.
'Versatile' screenshot ©Logotron.

Contents

Autumn term

Spring term

Introduction

Maths Action Plans (MAPs) is a series of practical teacher's resource books, four for each year of the primary school from Year 3/P4 to Year 6/P7. Each book contains lesson plans designed to help you to plan and deliver well-structured lessons in line with the National Numeracy Strategy *Framework for Teaching Mathematics* (1999).

MAPs is different from other lesson-plan based resource books because each title in the series focuses upon a different strand of mathematics at a particular year, thereby offering you a more coherent, "joined-up" approach to the teaching of key mathematical concepts. The activities in this book cover mathematical topics within the "Measures, shape and space" strand.

The MAPs lessons will encourage the children to organise their thinking about problems, select appropriate operations, explain their reasoning and suggest alternative methods. Lessons addressing other strands in the mathematics curriculum, namely "Solving Problems and Handling Data"; "Number" and "Calculations", can be found in companion titles in this series.

Planning – adopting or adapting

Although these books focus on specific mathematics topics, they also offer a bank of lessons that give complete coverage in line with the *Framework for Teaching Mathematics Sample Medium Term Planner* (2000). Every objective is tackled and the number of lessons matches the number of lessons in the planner exactly. This means that MAPs can be used as a complete core mathematics programme. Alternatively, the lessons can be used as additional plans for an existing scheme of work. Where fresh ideas or alternative approaches are desired then the lessons in MAPs can fit the bill.

To adapt or personalise the MAPs lessons to meet your needs, you might consider the following actions:
- select and copy individual MAPs lessons or units to supplement lessons/units that you have already
- add your own prepared resources to those recommended in the plans
- check that the lessons match the needs of the children in your class and, if necessary, substitute lessons for MAPs lessons from other years for more or less confident children
- work on the first lessons of a unit, then plan the use of supplementary activities as a stimulus for extension work or as the starting points for subsequent whole class lessons.

The intention throughout is to provide fresh ideas for planning the content, pace and pitch of your lessons within a framework that can be adopted or adapted to meet your needs and the needs of your class.

Curriculum planner

The lessons in this book have been written in line with the *Framework for Teaching Mathematics Sample Medium Term Planner* (2000).

The opening page of each unit includes the following information, which can be used in your medium term plans:

Framework links
This chart highlights the coverage of the NNS objectives and establishes the expectations of the unit.

Setting the scene
This section highlights the ideas underpinning the unit and any key mathematical concepts that are emphasised in the unit.

Starting points
This section identifies the knowledge and mathematical skills that children should have attained before tackling the lessons of this unit.

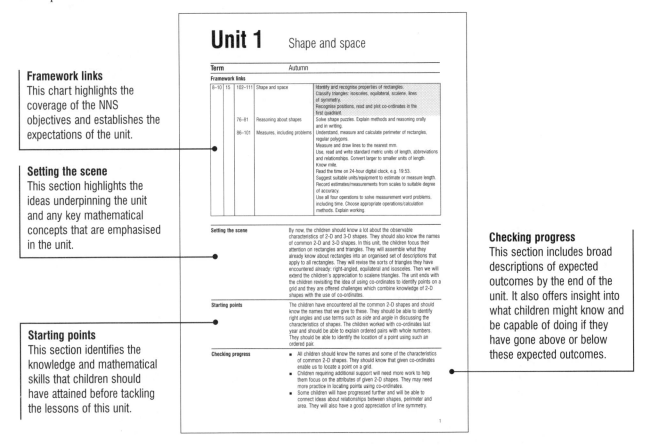

Checking progress
This section includes broad descriptions of expected outcomes by the end of the unit. It also offers insight into what children might know and be capable of doing if they have gone above or below these expected outcomes.

For each topic area, the MAPs have been carefully planned to ensure that lessons meet the requirements of teachers in Scotland and Wales given in the attainment targets both for *National Guidelines 5–14* in Scotland and in *Mathematics in the National Curriculum in Wales*. A correlation chart for *National Guidelines 5–14* in Scotland is presented on page viii. A correlation chart for *Mathematics in the National Curriculum in Wales* can be accessed on the following website: www.nelsonthornes.com/primary.

Differentiation

MAPs offers a controlled level of differentiation as the National Numeracy Strategy recommends. This can be by task, through assessed outcomes and/or suggestions for planning on the basis of prior knowledge or experience. Each lesson contains "support" or "challenge" ideas which offer an alternative route for individuals, pairs or groups.

Assessment

The learning objectives for each lesson are clearly stated and assessment opportunities are offered throughout in many of the pupil activities and resource sheets. Make time to observe the children as they work at these tasks during the main part of the lesson. Identify whether children have understood the concept or whether they have any misconceptions that need to be addressed. You might at this stage plan the use of additional support or challenge materials identified in each plan.

During the plenary, key questions are offered to provide important assessment information to guide teaching and planning. These should be supplemented by the use of open questions such as *How did you work that out? What if … ?* and *Are there other ways of working this out?*

Finally, for medium-term assessment, additional tasks can be planned for individual pupils or small groups during the half-termly "assess and review" lessons using pupil activities or the supplementary activities at the end of each unit.

The MAPs lesson

The plans are intended as a support for the daily mathematics lesson for the school mathematics co-ordinator, teacher and classroom assistant working within a particular group. Each lesson includes the following sections:

Learning objectives
This section gives the explicit targets for each lesson including oral and mental starters.

Mental/oral starter
There are a balance of oral and mental objectives across each title. Some are free-standing, others link to the main activity.

Main activity
Detailed guidance is given here which covers the main part of each lesson, including a description and organisation of the activity and a range of ideas for differentiating each lesson. Key questions are highlighted in italics.

Plenary
Key questions are highlighted here in italics to guide the structure of each plenary session. Opportunities are provided to assess pupils' progress and compare strategies used. Each plenary will help you to guide outcomes referenced to the learning objectives of the lesson.

Key fact or strategy
This section provides a summary of key facts learned or strategies that the children might have used. It also includes links to other areas of mathematics or to applications in other subjects including practical, everyday applications.

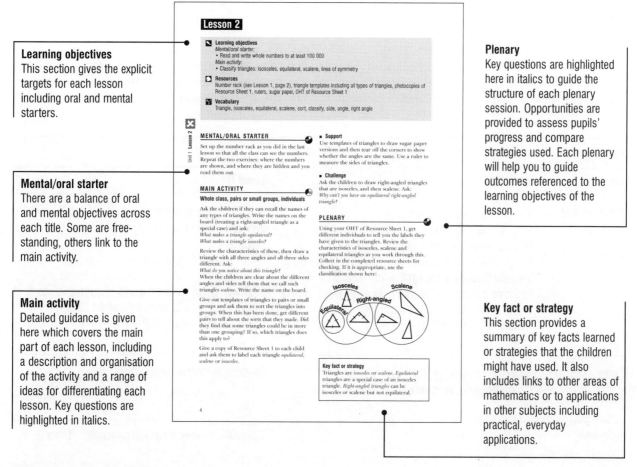

Supplementary activities

Fresh ideas are provided here, with further exemplification, different approaches, homework opportunities...

Homework
Weekly homework opportunities are described here, covering the objectives of the unit.

Development
This section gives ideas to develop the topic or objective over a period of time.

ICT ideas
This section includes general ideas of how to use ICT to support the teaching and learning of the mathematics in each unit. The section also includes some specific activities and software recommendations.

Mental/oral follow-up
For subsequent teaching, additional oral and mental activities are suggested here so that mental strategies that have been taught in the MAPs lessons can be practised, reinforced or developed further.

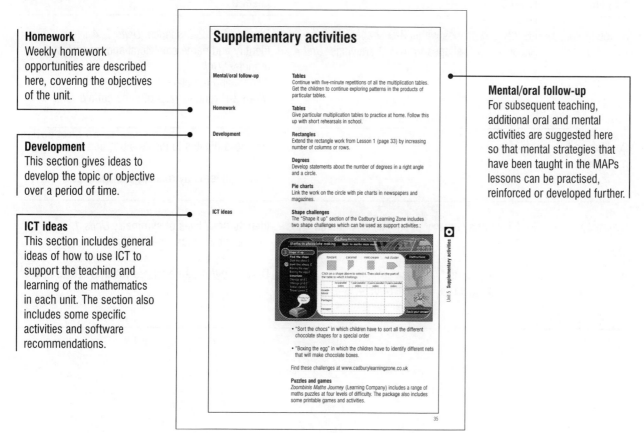

Scottish correlations

In these curriculum planner charts, no reference has been made to the activity at the beginning of each lesson in the book, namely the Mental/oral starter. These are designed to augment the numeracy and mathematical understanding of the children. They are wide-ranging and often address different objectives from those set down for the Main activities of each lesson. It is possible for teachers in Scottish schools to select from the Mental/oral starters those which match their pupil's learning and teaching needs.

Additionally, at the end of each unit of this book there are Supplementary activities and suggestions for using ICT. These will support work related to not only the Attainment targets for Number, money and measurement and Shape, position and movement, but also the Information handling target.

Number, money and measurement attainment target

Strands	Level C	Level D
Measure and estimate	Weight – include 20 g weights 1 kg = 1 000 g *Unit 6* Volume – litre, ½ litre, ¼ litre *Unit 9* Area – shapes composed of rectangles, squares or irregular shapes using cm² or m² *Unit 6* Estimate length and height in standard units *Unit 3* Select measuring devices and units *Unit 3* Read scales *Units 6, 9*	Length – mm, m *Unit 3* Weight – extend range *Unit 6* Volume – ml 1 l = 1 000 ml *Unit 9* Estimate small weights, areas, volumes *Units 6, 9* Select devices and units for weight *Unit 6* Imperial units *Units 3, 9*
Time	Simple timetables *Unit 3* Conventions for recording time *Unit 9*	24-hour timetable *Units 3, 9*
Perimeter, formulae, scales		Calculate perimeter by adding lengths *Units 3, 8*

Shape, position and movement attainment target

Strands	Level C	Level D
Range of shapes	Identify 2-D shapes within 3-D shapes *Unit 4* Recognise 3-D shapes from 2-D drawings *Unit 4*	Discuss 3-D/2-D shapes *Units 1, 4* Identify and name equilateral and isosceles triangles *Unit 1* Tiling using template *Units 2, 8* Make 3-D models/nets of cube/cuboid *Unit 4*
Position and movement		Use co-ordinates to locate a position on a grid *Unit 1* Create patterns by rotating a shape *Unit 4*
Symmetry	Find lines of symmetry of shapes on squared grids *Units 7*	Identify/draw lines of symmetry *Units 1, 7* Create symmetrical shapes *Unit 7*
Angle	Use "right", "acute", "obtuse" *Unit 4* Know a straight line = 180° *Units 4, 5*	Draw/copy/measure angles within 5° *Units 4, 5*

Unit 1   Shape and space

Term			Autumn	

Framework links

8–10	15	102–111	Shape and space	Identify and recognise properties of rectangles. Classify triangles: isosceles, equilateral, scalene, lines of symmetry. Recognise positions, read and plot co-ordinates in the first quadrant.
		76–81	Reasoning about shapes	Solve shape puzzles. Explain methods and reasoning orally and in writing.
		86–101	Measures, including problems	Understand, measure and calculate perimeter of rectangles, regular polygons. Measure and draw lines to the nearest mm. Use, read and write standard metric units of length, abbreviations and relationships. Convert larger to smaller units of length. Know mile. Read the time on 24-hour digital clock, e.g. 19:53. Suggest suitable units/equipment to estimate or measure length. Record estimates/measurements from scales to suitable degree of accuracy. Use all four operations to solve measurement word problems, including time. Choose appropriate operations/calculation methods. Explain working.

Setting the scene

By now, the children should know a lot about the observable characteristics of 2-D and 3-D shapes. They should also know the names of common 2-D and 3-D shapes. In this unit, the children focus their attention on rectangles and triangles. They will assemble what they already know about rectangles into an organised set of descriptions that apply to all rectangles. They will revise the sorts of triangles they have encountered already: right-angled, equilateral and isosceles. Then we will extend the children's appreciation to scalene triangles. The unit ends with the children revisiting the idea of using co-ordinates to identify points on a grid and they are offered challenges which combine knowledge of 2-D shapes with the use of co-ordinates.

Starting points

The children have encountered all the common 2-D shapes and should know the names that we give to these. They should be able to identify right angles and use terms such as *side* and *angle* in discussing the characteristics of shapes. The children worked with co-ordinates last year and should be able to explain ordered pairs with whole numbers. They should be able to identify the location of a point using such an ordered pair.

Checking progress

- All children should know the names and some of the characteristics of common 2-D shapes. They should know that given co-ordinates enable us to locate a point on a grid.
- Children requiring additional support will need more work to help them focus on the attributes of given 2-D shapes. They may need more practice in locating points using co-ordinates.
- Some children will have progressed further and will be able to connect ideas about relationships between shapes, perimeter and area. They will also have a good appreciation of line symmetry.

Lesson 1

◢ Learning objectives
Mental/oral starter:
• Read and write whole numbers to at least 100 000
Main activity:
• Identify and recognise properties of rectangles

📖 Resources
Number rack (see Mental/oral starter for instructions), individual whiteboards and pens or rough paper, variety of shape templates, pinboards (of different sizes if possible), rubber bands, photocopies of General Resource Sheet A, rulers, sharp pencils

ᵃᵇᶜ Vocabulary
Shape names of the templates that you use, rectangle, angle, right angle, side, equal, parallel, diagonal

MENTAL/ORAL STARTER

Before the lesson, prepare a number rack. First, cut 50 digit cards like this:

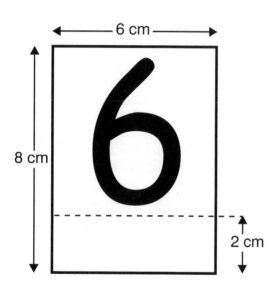

On the cards, using a wide felt-tipped pen, write in the digits 0 to 9 to make five sets of digit cards. Make each digit sit at least 2 cm from the bottom edge of the card.

Next, cut a piece of card 30 cm × 20 cm. Rule lines across it as shown here:

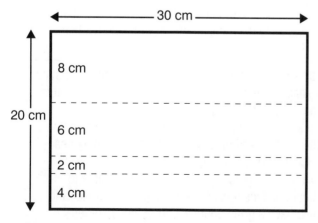

Score the lines across the card, then fold:

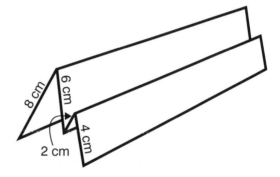

Use the rack to set up and display numbers from 1 to 100 000:

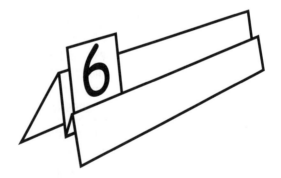

Set up the number rack so that all the class can see the numbers. Pick up digit cards from the shuffled pile and place them on show. Ask the children to tell you the name of each of the numbers that are created (vary between four-digit and five-digit numbers). When you have done a few, turn the stand away from the class, put up some cards and read the number to the class. The children should write down the number that you have said on individual whiteboards or rough paper. Get different children to show what they have written.

MAIN ACTIVITY 35

Whole class, pairs or small groups

Place shape templates on the OHP one at a time and ask the children to tell you the name of the shape. Ask:
How do you know?
Finish by putting a rectangle on the OHP and tell the children that you want them to concentrate on rectangles in this lesson.

Give out the equipment to pairs or small groups, telling the children that you want them to make some rectangles with the pinboards and rubber bands and then carefully copy them on General Resource Sheet A using rulers and sharp pencils. When the children have done this, ask them to tell you what they notice about the angles of a rectangle. Then get the children to look at the sides of each rectangle. Say:
There are two things about the sides. What are they?

When you have appropriate responses about length and the fact that opposite sides are parallel, remind the children, using a drawing on the board, about *diagonals*. Ask the children to draw in the diagonals on their rectangles and then they should measure these. Ask:
Are they the same length?
Where do they cross?

Use some examples from the class to discuss lengths and the fact that the diagonals cross at the centre of the rectangle. Ask:
How can we check that it is the centre?
Allow the children to do some measurement to support their suggestions.

■ Support

Using rectangle templates, let the children draw around these and tell you about each one. Get them to draw in the diagonals and measure the length of each one. Discuss where the *middle* of the rectangle is.

■ Challenge

Ask the children to draw some quadrilaterals and the diagonals in these. Ask:
Are the diagonals the same lengths? If not why not? What are the lengths from the point where they cross? Are there any patterns?

PLENARY 10

Review the characteristics of rectangles and produce a chart like this one that the children should note in their books:

Angles	• all four angles are right angles
Sides	• opposite sides are equal in length • opposite sides are parallel
Diagonals	• diagonals are the same length • diagonals cross at the centre • each part of the diagonal from the centre is the same length

Key fact or strategy
Regardless of size, all rectangles have the same characteristics.

Unit 1 **Lesson 1**

Lesson 2

◣ Learning objectives

Mental/oral starter:
- Read and write whole numbers to at least 100 000

Main activity:
- Classify triangles: isosceles, equilateral, scalene, lines of symmetry

◆ Resources

Number rack (see Lesson 1, page 2), triangle templates including all types of triangles, photocopies of Resource Sheet 1, rulers, sugar paper, OHT of Resource Sheet 1

ᵃᵇᶜ Vocabulary

Triangle, isosceles, equilateral, scalene, sort, classify, side, angle, right angle

MENTAL/ORAL STARTER ⑩

Set up the number rack as you did in the last lesson so that all the class can see the numbers. Repeat the two exercises: where the numbers are shown, and where they are hidden and you read them out.

MAIN ACTIVITY ㉟

Whole class, pairs or small groups, individuals

Ask the children if they can recall the names of any types of triangles. Write the names on the board (treating a right-angled triangle as a special case) and ask:
What makes a triangle equilateral?
What makes a triangle isosceles?

Review the characteristics of these, then draw a triangle with all three angles and all three sides different. Ask:
What do you notice about this triangle?
When the children are clear about the different angles and sides tell them that we call such triangles *scalene*. Write the name on the board.

Give out templates of triangles to pairs or small groups and ask them to sort the triangles into groups. When this has been done, get different pairs to tell about the sorts that they made. Did they find that some triangles could be in more than one grouping? If so, which triangles does this apply to?

Give a copy of Resource Sheet 1 to each child and ask them to label each triangle *equilateral, scalene* or *isosceles*.

■ Support

Use templates of triangles to draw sugar paper versions and then tear off the corners to show whether the angles are the same. Use a ruler to measure the sides of triangles.

■ Challenge

Ask the children to draw right-angled triangles that are isosceles, and then scalene. Ask:
Why can't you have an equilateral right-angled triangle?

PLENARY ⑩

Using your OHT of Resource Sheet 1, get different individuals to tell you the labels they have given to the triangles. Review the characteristics of isosceles, scalene and equilateral triangles as you work through this. Collect in the completed resource sheets for checking. If it is appropriate, use the classification shown here:

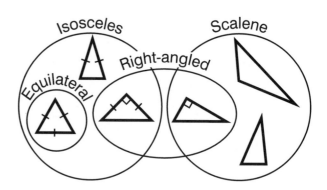

Key fact or strategy

Triangles are *isosceles* or *scalene*. *Equilateral* triangles are a special case of an isosceles triangle. *Right-angled triangles* can be isosceles or scalene but not equilateral.

Lesson 3

Learning objectives
Mental/oral starter:
- Count on and back in equal steps

Main activity:
- Classify triangles: isosceles, equilateral, scalene, lines of symmetry

Resources
Pinboards, rubber bands, rulers, sharp pencils, General Resource Sheet A, OHT of Resource Sheet 2, sugar paper, scissors

Vocabulary
Triangle, isosceles, scalene, equilateral, right angle, square, line of symmetry

MENTAL/ORAL STARTER

Ask the children to help you count on from 0 to 1000 in 100s. Now ask them to count back from 200 in 25s. Next count on in 5s from 0 to 100.

Tell the children that you now want to count up to 10, starting from 0, using 0.5s. To link this to the ×5 table, get the children to tell you the table while you write it on the board. Then ask them to count again in 0.5s to 10. Can they see the connection with the table? Finish by asking the children to count back from 7.5 to 3.5 in 0.5s.

MAIN ACTIVITY

Whole class, pairs, individuals

Ask the children to name the different types of triangle that they worked with in the last lesson. Write *equilateral, isosceles* and *scalene* on the board and ask:
What are the characteristics of each of these?
Tell the children that you want them to make and draw some triangles in this lesson.

Give out pinboards, rubber bands, rulers, sharp pencils and General Resource Sheet A (one each) to pairs of children. Ask them to make some different triangles on the pinboard and then use a ruler and pencil to draw each one carefully on the dotty paper. They should label each triangle to say what type of triangle it is. Give time for pairs to do at least five triangles.

When the children are ready, display the OHT of Resource Sheet 2. Ask the children to look at the drawing of the isosceles triangle. Ask:
Does this triangle have any lines of symmetry?
Discuss this and draw in the one line of symmetry when the children are at that stage.

Now do the same with the equilateral triangle:

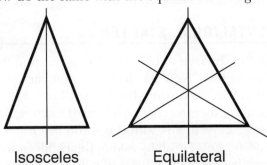

Isosceles   Equilateral

Ask about scalene triangles. (These have no lines of symmetry.) Now ask the children to draw in the lines of symmetry that there are (if any) in the triangles that they have drawn on the dotty paper. Collect the work in for checking.

■ Support
Cut out triangles from sugar paper and fold these to show the lines of symmetry.

■ Challenge
When lines of symmetry are drawn in, smaller triangles are created. Ask the children to identify what sorts of triangles these are.

PLENARY

Draw a table on the board as shown here and ask the children to help you complete it. Get the children to copy the table into their books.

Name	Facts about sides	Facts about angles	Facts about lines of symmetry
Isosceles			
Equilateral			
Scalene			

Key fact or strategy
Scalene triangles have no lines of symmetry.

5

Lesson 4

Learning objectives
Mental/oral starter:
• Count on and back in equal steps
Main activity:
• Recognise positions, read and plot co-ordinates in the first quadrant

Resources
OHT of General Resource Sheet B, OHT pens and cloth, photocopies of Resource Sheet 3, rulers, sharp pencils, OHT of Resource Sheet 3, photocopies of Resource Sheet 4, coloured pencils, OHT of Resource Sheet 4

Vocabulary
Co-ordinates, plot, square, scalene triangle, isosceles triangle, equilateral triangle, rectangle, pentagon, hexagon, other 2-D shape names chosen by the children

MENTAL/ORAL STARTER

Ask the children to help you count on from 0 to 1 000 in 100s. Now ask them to count back from 200 in 25s. Next count from 0 to 10 in 0.1s. Then ask them to count up from 0 to 20 in 0.2s (use ×2 table to link with this if you feel it appropriate). Finish by asking the children to count back from 6.8 to 4.4 in 0.2s.

MAIN ACTIVITY

Whole class, individuals, pairs

Using the OHT of General Resource Sheet B, ask the children to tell you what they can remember about co-ordinates. As ideas come, draw and label the axes and then ask for some points on the grid and the co-ordinates that describe the position of each point. Do this for a number of points until you feel that the children are fully aware of the rule that we use the horizontal axis numbers followed by the vertical axis numbers.

Give out Resource Sheet 3, rulers and sharp pencils. Ask the children to work on their own in naming the co-ordinates for each of the given shapes. When the children have done this, display your OHT of Resource Sheet 3 and ask different individuals to solve each of the questions. Use this opportunity to review the understanding of the conventions for marking axes and writing and reading co-ordinates.

Give out Resource Sheet 4 and sharp coloured pencils to pairs of children. Tell the children to mark the points on each of the grids that the co-ordinates describe. Then they should draw the shape and write down its name.

■ Support
Draw a range of common 2-D shapes on the OHT of General Resource Sheet B and get the co-ordinates listed by the class or a group.

■ Challenge
Ask the children to write co-ordinates for other shapes that they choose.

PLENARY

Display your OHT of Resource Sheet 4. Ask different pairs to help you place the co-ordinates and draw the shape. Ask: *What is the name of the shape?*

Finish by asking the children to work out co-ordinates for another shape and give you these to see if you can draw the shape. *What is its name?*

Key fact or strategy
Co-ordinates are always written and read using the number along the horizontal axis followed by the number along the vertical axis.

Lesson 5

🔧 Learning objectives
Mental/oral starter:
- Round any three- or four-digit number to the nearest 10 or 100

Main activitiy:
- Recognise positions, read and plot co-ordinates in the first quadrant

📓 Resources
Number rack (see Lesson 1, page 2), photocopies of Resource Sheet 5, rulers, sharp pencils or coloured pencils, OHT of Resource Sheet 5, OHT pens and cloth, photocopies of Resource Sheet 6, OHT of Resource Sheet 6

🔤 Vocabulary
Co-ordinates, plot, point, vertex, vertices, square, trapezium, rectangle, parallelogram, quadrilateral, shape names chosen by the children

MENTAL/ORAL STARTER   ⏱10

Using your number rack, make some three-digit then some four-digit numbers. For each number ask the children:
What is this rounded to the nearest 10?
What is it rounded to the nearest 100?

Get individuals to come out and make numbers and tell you what it is to the nearest 10 and 100. Get the class to check each time.

MAIN ACTIVITY   ⏱35

Whole class, pairs

Revise the conventions for using co-ordinates. Tell the children that in this lesson they are going to have to find some missing co-ordinates using clues that they will be given. Give Resource Sheet 5 to pairs of children together with rulers and sharp pencils or coloured pencils. Use the first example to work through what has to be done; if necessary use the OHT of Resource Sheet 5 to work out the answer for the whole class. Then ask the children to find the missing co-ordinates and draw the named shapes.

Using the OHT, get different pairs to give their solutions and draw the shapes. Is there any confusion? If so, take the opportunity once more to revise how co-ordinates should be read and written.

Give out Resource Sheet 6, again to pairs. Ask the children to label the axes and draw some quadrilaterals, then determine the co-ordinates for these. They should then prepare some questions like those on Resource Sheet 5 with a missing co-ordinate.

■ Support
Revise vocabulary as necessary, including shape names and the characteristics of the shapes.

■ Challenge
Ask the children to work out how many co-ordinates they would need to give so that someone could draw a *regular* pentagon or hexagon.

PLENARY   ⏱10

Put your OHT of Resource Sheet 6 on display. Ask a pair to give a set of three co-ordinates and get the class to help you find the missing co-ordinate. When this has been done ask:
What is the name of this shape?

Then ask the pair whose question it is to tell you whether you and the class have got it right. Repeat as many times as is fruitful.

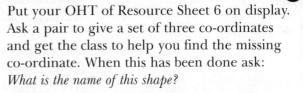

Key fact or strategy
Some 2-D shapes can be drawn on the basis of part information but others cannot unless one accepts different forms of a shape. For example, giving two co-ordinates for an isosceles triangle will allow such triangles to be drawn but there are an infinite number of correct third co-ordinates.

Supplementary activities

Mental/oral follow-up

Number rack
Continue to use the number rack (see Lesson 1, page 2) for exercises about reading, writing and rounding numbers.

Tables beyond x10
Review multiplication tables and use some of these to count on products, then extend the tables by counting beyond the product of the 10s. For example, counting on in fives beyond the product of 10 x 5 gives us 55, 60, 65, and so on. These are the same as 11 x 5, 12 x 5, 13 x 5, and so on. The children might be interested in the fact that we used to have to learn tables to x12 because we used feet and inches (there are twelve inches in a foot). They may also like to know that children in the USA still have to learn the x11 and x12 because they continue to use feet and inches.

Homework

Rectangles
Give Resource Sheet 7 as a revision exercise about the characteristics of rectangles. For some children you might also choose to give Resource Sheet 8.

Development

Making rectangles
Investigations about rectangles can be useful. For example, combining squares to make rectangles and seeing how many different rectangles can be made with a given number of squares. Resource Sheet 9 has such challenges and extends the work into looking at polyominoes. You may choose to leave this until the children are in Year 6.

Line symmetry
Get the children to make collections of logos that display line symmetry. Take the children on a photo shoot around school to identify and photograph parts of the building or grounds that have built objects with line symmetry.

Real co-ordinates
Start the children on using co-ordinates for finding places on real maps. Use local Ordnance Survey maps to do this. At first, choose places that are on the intersection of horizontal and vertical lines then choose some places that are in the centre of squares. In talking about these you could use fractions, for example, (45½, 75½).

Distorted grids
There are interesting shape and space possibilities if you "distort" grids and then use co-ordinates. Such distortions can be very helpful in getting the children to really understand the conventions about co-ordinates. Examples are offered in Resource Sheets 10 and 11. One or both of these resource sheets could be given as extension work or homework for some children.

ICT ideas

Rectangles

Can Do Maths Year 5/P6 CD-ROM 3 (Nelson Thornes) includes two activities covering the properties of rectangles. In activity 1, children are presented with a series of statements about rectangles which they have to identify as "true" or "false". If a child classifies a statement incorrectly, then a helpful demonstration is given to show why the classification is incorrect. Activity 2 offers a simple sorting exercise, though children's understanding of the properties of rectangles is tested by presenting a range of "thin" rectangles, squares, rectangles in unusual orientations, shapes that differ from rectangles in only one attribute and so on.

Unit 2   Reasoning about shapes

Term				Autumn

Framework links

8–10	15	102–111	Shape and space	Identify and recognise properties of rectangles. Classify triangles: isosceles, equilateral, scalene, lines of symmetry. Recognise positions, read and plot co-ordinates in the first quadrant.
		76–81	Reasoning about shapes	Solve shape puzzles. Explain methods and reasoning orally and in writing.
		86–101	Measures, including problems	Understand, measure and calculate perimeter of rectangles, regular polygons. Measure and draw lines to the nearest mm. Use, read and write standard metric units of length, abbreviations and relationships. Convert larger to smaller units of length. Know mile. Read the time on 24-hour digital clock, e.g. 19:53. Suggest suitable units/equipment to estimate or measure length. Record estimates/measurements from scales to suitable degree of accuracy. Use all four operations to solve measurement word problems, including time. Choose appropriate operations/calculation methods. Explain working.

Setting the scene

Reasoning about shapes offers good opportunities for discussion. It supports the children in articulating general ideas about mathematics. The fact that there is a visual, and often tactile, component helps many children formulate such ideas. In this unit, the connecting shape is the square. The first lesson focuses on making rectangles using squares. The second reinforces work done on area previously and gives the opportunity for the children to meet one key requirement, that of describing a procedure, in this case about the area of rectangles.

Starting points

The children should know all common shape names and have had experience in calculating areas from counting squares.

Checking progress

- All children should be able to determine the number of rectangles that can be made from a given number of squares. They should also be able to count squares to obtain a measure of area.
- Children requiring additional support will need help in recognising similar rectangles.
- Some children will have progressed further and will be able to develop ideas about pattern and relationships.

Lesson 1

MENTAL/ORAL STARTER

Write the digits 0 to 9 on the board and ask everyone to choose one and write it down on rough paper. Randomly select three children and ask what their chosen numbers are. Write down a number that can be made from these three digits. Ask the class to tell you what this number would be rounded to the nearest 10, then 100. Repeat as often as you wish.

Now tell the class a three-digit number that ends in 0 and ask them to tell you any numbers that they can think of that would round to this number. For example, 290 would be the result of rounding 285 to 289 and 291 to 294. Repeat as often as you wish.

MAIN ACTIVITY

Whole class, pairs or small groups

Using six squares, ask the children how many different rectangles you can make. There are two: six squares in a row, and three squares by two rows. Show that two squares by three rows is not a different rectangle by drawing the possible rectangles on the board.

Now give out squares and General Resource Sheet C to pairs or small groups. Tell them to use twelve squares and see how many different rectangles can be made this time. The results should be recorded on the squared paper. You need very many squares for this activity, and if there are not enough, consider differentiating the task asking some children to work on squared paper without using templates.

When the children have drawn the three possible rectangles, display those of several different groups.

Then invite the children to choose another even number of squares and see how many rectangles

they can make. Ask the children:
Why should it be an even number of squares?

■ Support
Work with groups to create the two different rectangles possible from six squares pointing out why they are different and showing rotations as not being different.

■ Challenge
See whether children can make the link to factors and multiples, or at least to multiplication tables. For example, factors of twelve are one, two, three, four, six and twelve. Using these to make twelve, we have 1×12, 2×6 and 3×4 (the three rectangles).

PLENARY

Ask what numbers of squares have been tried. Choose some of these and ask the appropriate groups to tell the class what they have found. If anyone has done 24 squares make sure to include this in the discussion. Ask:
Can anyone tell me about any connection that they have spotted between the number of squares and multiplication?

Collect in the work for evaluation purposes.

Key fact or strategy
The rectangles must be different (rotations are not allowed) so, for example, a 3×4 and a 4×3 rectangle are the same in this exercise.

Lesson 2

Unit 2 Lesson 2

☙ Learning objectives

Mental/oral starter:
- Round any three- or four-digit number to the nearest 10 or 100

Main activity:
- Solve shape puzzles. Explain methods and reasoning orally and in writing

📖 Resources

Photocopies of Resource Sheets 12 and 13, rulers

🔤 Vocabulary

Square, rectangle, area, square centimetre, cm^2

MENTAL/ORAL STARTER

This exercise is identical to that of the last lesson except you should choose four children each time to make four-digit numbers. Also give four-digit numbers ending in 0 and then ending in 00 as the last part of the exercise.

MAIN ACTIVITY

Whole class, pairs or small groups, individuals

Remind the children about work that they have previously done on area, particularly counting squares as a means to determine and make comparisons of areas.

Give out Resource Sheet 12 and ask pairs or small groups to determine the areas of the rectangles on the sheet.

When the children have done this, ask how they managed the task. Get different pairs or groups to explain to the class the approaches used. Draw a rectangle on the board telling the children that it measures 10 cm long and 5 cm wide. Ask:
How can you work out its area?

When you have an explanation about multiplying length by breadth or width write this on the board. Get the children to write it down too.

Now give out Resource Sheet 13 and ask the children to do this individually using the rule that they have written down.

■ Support

Do some practical work on counting squares if necessary.

■ Challenge

Get the children to draw some rectangles whose sides are not in complete centimetres. Can they use the rule to work out the areas of these rectangles?

PLENARY

Work through Resource Sheet 13 using different individuals to take the lead on each of the rectangles. Keep reinforcing the method used. Collect in sheets for marking.

> **Key fact or strategy**
> Multiplying length by breadth gives us the area of a rectangle.

Supplementary activities

Mental/oral follow-up

Rounding
The final exercises in both lessons where the children have a target number then have to deduce all the numbers that would round to the target is well worth repeating.

Homework

Area
Choose a selection of cuboids at home (such as cereal boxes, books, shoeboxes, and so on). Then using the rule developed in class and a centimetre ruler, the children can work out the areas of some of the faces.

Development

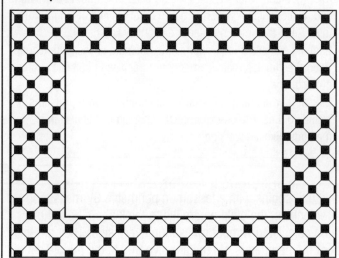

Area of compound shapes
Using different rectangles, make up some compound shapes in the shape of, for example, a T, an F and an E. Can the children divide the shape into rectangles and then calculate area? Try a small rectangle inside a larger one to make a rectangular path like the one here.
Can the children work out the area of the path?

ICT ideas

2-D shapes
A "binary tree" program such as *Granada Branch* (Granada Learning) can be used to sort and classify different 2-D shapes. By providing "yes" and "no" answers to questions they have to formulate themselves, children learn to divide shapes into subsets, which are gradually built into binary trees on-screen. These can be saved by the pupils and printed out.

Puzzles and games
Zoombinis Maths Journey (Learning Company) includes a range of maths puzzles at four levels of difficulty. The package also includes some printable games and activities.

Unit 3 Measures and time

Term Autumn

Framework links

8–10	15	102–111	Shape and space	Identify and recognise properties of rectangles. Classify triangles: isosceles, equilateral, scalene, lines of symmetry. Recognise positions, read and plot co-ordinates in the first quadrant.
		76–81	Reasoning about shapes	Solve shape puzzles. Explain methods and reasoning orally and in writing.
		86–101	Measures, including problems	Understand, measure and calculate perimeter of rectangles, regular polygons. Measure and draw lines to the nearest mm. Use, read and write standard metric units of length, abbreviations and relationships. Convert larger to smaller units of length. Know mile. Read the time on 24-hour digital clock, e.g. 19:53. Suggest suitable units/equipment to estimate or measure length. Record estimates/measurements from scales to suitable degree of accuracy. Use all four operations to solve measurement word problems, including time. Choose appropriate operations/calculation methods. Explain working.

Setting the scene

The work in this unit begins with a lesson on perimeter. By measuring the perimeters of rectangles, the children are led to think about how the perimeter can be calculated without measuring every side. They are then invited to look at the perimeters of regular polygons. In the middle set of lessons in the unit, they are working on measures of length. They practise measuring in millimetres, choose units with which to estimate and measure and confirm their knowledge of the relationship between metric units. The final lesson in the unit gives the children the opportunity to demonstrate that they can read time on a 24-hour digital clock.

Starting points

In Year 4/P5, the children will already have done some work on perimeters. They will have learned the relationships between standard metric units and common equivalent fractions of these. They will also have used standard units to estimate and measure length and recorded lengths in metres and centimetres in decimal form. Their knowledge of how to read clocks extended to a 12-hour digital and an analogue clock.

Checking progress

- All children should be able to measure or calculate the perimeter of a rectangle and know how to find the perimeter of a regular polygon. They should be able to suggest equipment and units to estimate or make measurements and convert larger metric units to smaller ones. They should be able to read a 24-hour digital clock.
- Children requiring additional support will benefit from extra practice in measuring perimeters, spelling out the relationships between metric units of length and reading both 12- and 24-hour digital clocks.
- Some children will have progressed further and be adept not only at describing how to calculate the perimeters of rectangles and regular polygons, but also in using metric and imperial units of length and interpreting times written in different formats.

Lesson 1

◤ Learning objectives
Mental/oral starter:
- Recall addition facts for each number up to 20

Main activity:
- Understand, measure and calculate the perimeter of rectangles and regular polygons

📖 Resources
Small whiteboards and whiteboard pens, addition pairs booklets made from Resource Sheets 14 and 15 (see Mental/oral starter for instructions), coloured chalk, photocopies of Resource Sheet 16, centimetre rulers, photocopies of Resource Sheet 17, OHT of Resource Sheet 18, photocopies of Resource Sheet 18

📝 Vocabulary
Perimeter, length, side, edge, polygon, regular polygon

MENTAL/ORAL STARTER

Choose a pair of children and ask them to work out all the ways they can to make two numbers between one and twenty using addition. Try giving them one and eleven. They should call out the answers, which should include these:

$1 \rightarrow 1 + 0, 0 + 1$

$11 \rightarrow 11 + 0, 10 + 1, 9 + 2, 8 + 3,$
$\qquad 7 + 4, 6 + 5, 5 + 6, 4 + 7,$
$\qquad 3 + 8, 2 + 9, 1 + 10, 0 + 11,$
$\qquad 3 + 6 + 2$ and others involving more than number pairs

When you have listed all their ideas, throw it open to the whole class to add to the list of bonds. Then choose another pair of children and pair of numbers. If, for example, two and twelve are chosen bonds such as $1 + 1$ and $1 + 11$ and $2 + 0$ and $2 + 10$ can be compared and discussed. Continue until all the numbers to twenty have been covered. Give time for children to write down their ideas on whiteboards, if appropriate.

Before or after mental/oral starters like this one, a book of addition pairs to make numbers to twenty can be made using Resource Sheets 14 and 15. These should be enlarged ×2 on A3 paper, one sheet on each side of the paper. The booklets can then be made up as shown here:

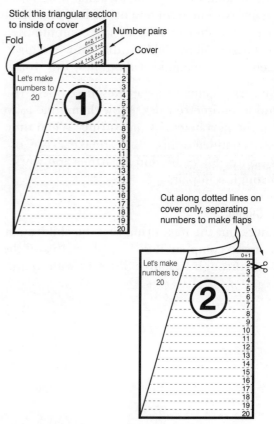

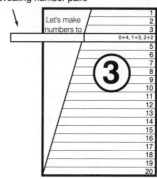

The children can fill in the number pairs if you do not wish to have the book ready made. These booklets are especially useful to support the less numerate children in the class.

MAIN ACTIVITY

Whole class, individuals, pairs

Draw a rectangle on the board and ask a child to come out and demonstrate what we mean by the *perimeter*. Then draw a number of polygons on the board (they need not be regular) and each time ask a child to show what is meant by the perimeter of the shape. They could use a coloured chalk to draw around the outline of each shape or trace around it with a finger.

Return to the rectangle shape and establish with the children that the characteristics of a rectangle include two pairs of sides of equal length. Talk through the idea that if we know the measurement of one of the longer sides and one of the shorter sides we can compute the perimeter. Allow children the chance to give their own explanations about how this works.

Give each child a copy of Resource Sheet 16 and a centimetre ruler. Allow them time to work out the perimeters by measuring. When they have completed this, they can take a copy of Resource Sheet 17, find a partner and work through it in pairs.

■ Support

Check out the measuring that the children are doing to complete Resource Sheet 16 and then work through Resource Sheet 17 with them.

■ Challenge

Ask children who complete both the resource sheets with ease to work out several possible values for the lengths of the sides of a rectangle with a perimeter of 60 cm.

PLENARY

Display the OHT of Resource Sheet 18. Discuss what we mean by a *polygon*, how we measure the perimeter of a regular polygon, and how we could compute the perimeter if we know the length of one side. Give the children a copy of Resource Sheet 18, on which they can write in their own idea about how to calculate the perimeter of a polygon. You may prefer to give this resource sheet for children to do at home, where they can measure and calculate the perimeters and then test out whether their own expression regarding perimeters of regular polygons works (See Homework, page 20).

Key fact or strategy

The perimeter of a rectangle is equal to twice the sum of the lengths of a longer and shorter side; and the perimeter of a regular polygon is found by multiplying one length of a side by the number of sides.

Unit 3 **Lesson 1**

Lesson 2

✎ Learning objectives
Mental/oral starter:
• Recall subtraction facts for each number up to 20
Main activity:
• Measure and draw lines to the nearest mm
• Use standard metric units of length and their abbreviations
• Record estimates/measurements from scales to a suitable degree of accuracy

📖 Resources
Millimetre rulers, photocopies of Resource Sheet 19, items to measure, access to a school corridor, selection of measuring tools, photocopies of Resource Sheet 20

ᵃᵦᶜ Vocabulary
Millimetre, centimetre, metre, mm, cm, m, unit of measurement, estimate

MENTAL/ORAL STARTER

Split the class into two teams, the odds and the evens. Say a number between one and twenty at random. The team whose number it is has to create as many different number pair subtractions to make that number (using numbers between zero and twenty) as they can. A different member of the team should provide each subtraction. Write up their answers on the board. When they have given you all their ideas, and if there are still number pairs to be found, allow the other team to complete them, for one point per number pair. Repeat this process with as many numbers as possible in turn.

MAIN ACTIVITY

Whole class, individuals, small groups, pairs

Hold up a ruler marked in millimetres. Ask the children what the markings on the ruler are. Establish that they remember the association between centimetres and millimetres. Talk about the importance of placing the starting point of the scale on the ruler against one end of a line to be measured. Give the children each a copy of Resource Sheet 19 and allow them time to complete it.

Before the class, set up a measuring workshop by choosing items to be measured using mm, cm and m. When the children have finished Resource Sheet 19, call the class together and talk through the workshop, so that they are reminded of the importance of choosing a unit that is appropriate for measuring a length and also the necessity of making an estimate before carrying through the measuring. Allow the children to work in groups, measuring the three items listed on Resource Sheet 20 and then

adding the items you have identified for measuring to the list. Circulate amongst the groups, identifying those who are experiencing difficulties. Ask children to make their own record of the measuring work on a copy of Resource Sheet 20.

■ Support
Supervise the children who find it difficult to measure accurately in millimetres, helping them to position the rule correctly and then read off from the scale.

■ Challenge
Children who complete the work on Resource Sheet 19 should share and compare their work with a partner.

PLENARY

Talk through the measuring workshop the children have done, checking misconceptions and discussing any problems the children had.

Key fact or strategy
Metric units for measuring length include mm, cm and m, and estimation is a powerful tool in helping us choose appropriate units of measurement.

Lesson 3

◣ Learning objectives
Mental/oral starter:
- Add and subtract pairs of two-digit numbers without crossing 100

Main activity:
- Use, read and write metric units of length and relationships.
- Convert larger to smaller units of length
- Know imperial units of length

▣ Resources
Calculators, photocopies of Resource Sheets 21 and 22, centimetre tapes

Vocabulary
Millimetre, mm, centimetre, cm, metre, m, kilometre, km, inch, foot, yard, mile

MENTAL/ORAL STARTER

Choose any two single digits, for example 6 and 7. Ask the children to add together 6 and 7, 16 and 17, 26 and 27, 36 and 37 and 46 and 47, thus:

```
6   +   7
16  +   17
26  +   27
36  +   37
46  +   47
```

Then take any other pair of digits, including the same digit twice, ensuring that the addition will not cross 100. Do this until the time allowed for mental/oral work is up.

MAIN ACTIVITY

Whole class, individuals, pairs

Talk through the relationships between metric measures. Begin by writing 10 cm on the board. Then ask:

How many millimetres here?
Can you say what fraction or decimal fraction this is of a metre? (¹⁄₁₀ or 0.1)
What fraction or decimal fraction of a kilometre? (¹⁄₁₀ ₀₀₀ or 0.0001)

This is rather tricky to work out orally, but a child could try to reach the answer on a calculator.

Use this discussion to establish the relationships between the units of metric measurement. To test the children's constructs of these concepts, give them some quick-fire questions to think about. Here are some examples:

Which is smaller: a millimetre or a centimetre?
What is the next biggest unit to a centimetre?
How many metres in two kilometres?
How many centimetres in two metres?

How many millimetres in two centimetres? …in twenty centimetres?

Write up the family chart of metric measures of length as shown at the top of Resource Sheet 22.

Change the discussion to focus on imperial measures, explaining the link between the inch, foot and mile. Write up the family of imperial measures of length on the board, as shown at the top of Resource Sheet 22.

Give out Resource Sheet 21 to individuals for them to tackle the conversions. When they have completed this the children can work in pairs to solve the puzzles on Resource Sheet 22.

■ Support
Allow these children to try the conversions on Resource Sheet 21 using calculators

■ Support
For children who complete both resource sheets, write up on the board a list of measurements that they can make using centimetre tapes and then convert into the imperial equivalent.

PLENARY

Review the families of metric and imperial measures of length, checking that the children can convert larger metric units into smaller metric units.

> ### Key fact or strategy
> Relationships between mm, cm, m, km and in, ft, yd and mile.

Lesson 4

Learning objectives
Mental/oral starter:
- Add or subtract pairs of two-digit numbers crossing 100

Main activity:
- Read the time on a 24-hour digital clock

Resources
Large 12-hour analogue clock, large 24-hour digital clock, photocopies of Resource Sheets 23 and 24, photocopies of Resource Sheet 25 on thin card, scissors

Vocabulary
Analogue clock, digital clock, 24-hour clock, 12-hour clock, hour, minute

MENTAL/ORAL STARTER

Choose a number between 100 and 200 and write it on the board. For example, you may choose 136. Now write up two 2-digit numbers that sum to 136. For example 45 and 91.

Then ask a child to give a different pair of 2-digit numbers totalling to 136. Continue to ask different children until you have about ten pairs of numbers. Then begin again with a new starting number.

MAIN ACTIVITY

Whole class, individuals, pairs

Show the children the 12-hour analogue clock. Give the children the name of it and show a time on the clock. If, for example, the time is 4 o'clock, discuss the fact that it could be 4 a.m. or 4 p.m. Compare this with the digital clock and discuss what this would read if the time was 4 p.m.

Hand out copies of Resource Sheet 23. You may need one between two or one each, depending on children's confidence with handling the 24-hour clock. Talk about how 4 p.m. and 16:00 would look on this clock face. Then give the children several oral challenges, asking individual children to describe where the hands on the face would be for examples such as half past nine in the evening, quarter past two, 15:30 or 18:00.

Give each child a copy of Resource Sheet 24 and tell them to fill in the times on the digital clocks.

In pairs, they should then take a copy of the game on Resource Sheet 25 and cut out all the individual cards to play some time games:
- **Time match:** spread out all the cards face up and take turns to choose a matching pair

- **Memory pairs:** turn all the shuffled cards face down. Take turns to turn over two cards, taking the pair if they match or turning them back over if they do not

- **Time Snap:** shuffle the cards and deal them all out. Take turns to put down a card, face up, on the pile. When two match, the first to call "Snap" takes all the cards in the face-up pile.

■ Support
Allow these children to use the clock face on Resource Sheet 23 to help them in completing Resource Sheet 24. Then sit with them while they play the first two of the games using Resource Sheet 25 cards.

■ Challenge
Ask the children to write out the time twenty-seven minutes past two, in as many ways as they can. Here are some:

Twenty-seven minutes past two
Two twenty-seven
Thirty-three minutes to three
2:27 a.m.
2:27 p.m.
02:27
14:27

PLENARY

Go through Resource Sheet 24, writing in the correct answers with the children's help.

Key fact or strategy
We can read and detect the difference between times shown as 4:15 a.m., 4:15 p.m., 04:15 and 16:15.

Supplementary activities

Mental/oral follow-up

Number pairs to twenty
Ask the children to help devise teaching aids to help them with number pair bonds for numbers to twenty.

Two-digit pairs
Choose a two-digit number and work out all the two-digit pairs of numbers that will sum to or subtract to the given start number.

See how many different two-digit number pairs sum to a three-digit number between 100 and 200.

Homework

Perimeters
Give the children a copy of Resource Sheet 18, on which they can measure and calculate the perimeters of the regular polygons. They can then test out whether their own expression regarding perimeters of regular polygons works.

Time games
Allow the children a copy of Resource Sheet 25 to take home so that they can cut out the time cards and play the games.

Development

Measurements in real life
Investigate which unit of measurement of length is most used in which profession. For example, architects and engineers may use the millimetre, those involved in fashion and clothes production may use the centimetre, fencing experts may deal in yards or metres, while racing drivers or racing cyclists use the kilometre or mile. The children could find out why it is that these people find the units they choose the most useful. This should lead on to the idea of degrees of accuracy.

Measurement game
Invite the children to create a game involving tools for measuring length and tasks for which they might be used. These can be used as playing cards or to support a board game. On Resource Sheet 26, there are some suggested tools and starting-point pictures to help children's thinking.

Estimate of the day
Create an "Estimate of the day" chart. Each day set a new task related to measuring lengths in and around the classroom. Use plenary time or time at the end of the day to discuss the children's estimates and the units of measurement they have chosen. Link this to the best tool for the job, if the measurement were carried through.

24-hour timetable
Ask the children to write a timetable for their day, using a 24-hour digital clock. They should include their before school and after school activities in the schedule.

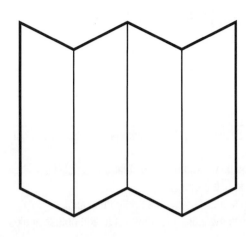

Which unit?
Ask the children to create a four-fold list by folding a piece of A4 paper into four crosswise to reveal four sections, as shown on the left:

They should head up the sections as shown here:

Millimetre	Centimetre	Metre	Kilometre

Then ask the children to list in each column as many things as they can which would be best measured using each unit of measurement.

ICT ideas

Time
Talking Clocks (Topologika) can be used by children to work out the time gap between any combination of analogue or digital clocks. The program uses sample speech and is fully configurable, so that you can prepare a different challenge for each session.

Measures and time
The Cadbury Zone web site offers "Maths in chocolate making", a selection of activities devised by BEAM. Within this area, "Journey Times" offers some differentiated activities involving mass and time.

Visit the site at www.cadburylearningzone.co.uk

Unit 3 **Supplementary activities**

Unit 4   Shape and space

| Term | | | | | Spring |

Framework links

5	8	102–111	Shape and space	Visualise 3-D shapes from 2-D drawings and identify nets of open cube.
				Recognise directions, and perpendicular and parallel lines.
				Understand and use degrees.
				Identify, estimate and order acute and obtuse angles.
				Use protractor to measure and draw acute and obtuse angles to 5˚.
				Make patterns from rotating shapes.
				Calculate angles in a straight line.
		76–81	Reasoning about shapes	Recognise and explain patterns and relationships, generalise and predict.

Setting the scene

One of the important skills that we all need to develop is the ability to visualise 3-D shapes from 2-D representations. We use this skill not just in mathematics, but in a variety of contexts, such as map-reading, using measuring jugs, making up models from parts, drawing and DIY. In this unit, the children work on this skill, extending it to an appreciation of nets and how these can be turned into given 3-D objects. This involves not only an appreciation of rotation but also the application of such terms as *horizontal, vertical, perpendicular*. Also in this unit, the children develop further their understanding of the different meanings of the term *angle* and how we measure angles using protractors. This work involves an understanding of both acute and obtuse angles. The theme of rotation is also continued.

Starting points

The children have by now had a lot of experiences with common 2-D and 3-D shapes and should be familiar with names and characteristics of these. They have also been expanding their shape and space vocabulary and should be able to use terms such as *diagonal* and *parallel* appropriately. Last term, the children worked on rectangles and triangles and, in doing this, discussed a variety of angles. This unit introduces the use of the protractor.

Checking progress

- All children should be able to name common 2-D and 3-D shapes and many of the characteristics of these. They should also know what a right angle is and that we can compare and contrast shapes using angles.
- Children requiring additional support will need opportunities to use 3-D shape-building materials and kits.
- Some children will have progressed further and will know that angles are measured in degrees.

Lesson 1

Learning objectives

Mental/oral starter:
- Count on/back in equal steps including beyond zero

Main activity:
- Review characteristics of 3-D shapes
- Visualise 3-D shapes from 2-D drawings

Resources

Resource Sheets 27 and 28 photocopied on card and cut out, sets of 3-D shapes (at least six of each shape), photocopies of Resource Sheet 29, OHT of Resource Sheet 29, OHT pen, photocopies of Resource Sheet 30, Multilink cubes or similar, photocopies of Resource Sheet 31

Vocabulary

Names of the 3-D shapes in your sets, face, edge, vertex, vertices, cube, cuboid

MENTAL/ORAL STARTER

Deal out the cards that you have made from Resource Sheet 27, one to each child in the class. Ask a child to state his start number, then count on or back using a step number that you give him from Resource Sheet 28 until you stop him. Continue as appropriate.

MAIN ACTIVITY

Whole class, pairs

Using one of the 3-D shapes, ask the children to tell you what is meant by *face*, *edge* and *vertex*. Ask:
What does vertices *mean?*

Give out sets of shapes or place different shapes around the room so that children can get a new one each time they have looked at a shape. Give out Resource Sheet 29 telling the children that you want them to work in pairs to complete the sheet. When the children have had time to do this, get the whole class together again and display the OHT of Resource Sheet 29. Ask different pairs to help as you work through the sheet.

Now give out Resource Sheet 30, telling the children:
These are drawings of piles of cubes. Can you work out how many cubes were needed to make each one?

When the children are ready, get different pairs to give their solutions. Where there are disagreements, use the Multilink cubes to make up the shape.

Finally move the children on to Resource Sheet 31, asking them to discuss with their partner how many cubes would have to be added to the

sets on the sheet to turn each shape into a cuboid. If the children do not reach the work on Resource Sheet 31, this could be given as homework or treated as a development activity.

■ Support

Use Multilink or similar to make the shapes on Resource Sheets 30 and 31.

■ Challenge

Ask the children to see if they can detect any patterns in the numbers of faces, edges and vertices of the given 3-D shapes.

PLENARY

Work through some of the examples on Resource Sheets 30 and 31 discussing how the children tackled these problems and what the answers are. Take in the work for checking.

Key fact or strategy

Cuboids can always be made from cubes.

Lesson 2

 Learning objectives

Mental/oral starter:
- Recall addition and subtraction facts for each number up to 20

Main activity:
- Visualise 3-D shapes from 2-D drawings
- Identify nets of an open cube

 Resources
Parallel number lines display (see Mental/oral starter for instructions) or OHT with parallel number lines, rubber bands or OHT pen and a ruler, large open cube that can be taken apart, photocopies of Resource Sheet 32, scissors, coloured pencils, photocopies of Resource Sheet 33, OHT of Resource Sheet 33, OHT pen

Vocabulary
Cube, open cube, net

MENTAL/ORAL STARTER

Before the lesson, make a parallel number lines display as shown below and attach it to a backing or display board, or prepare an OHT with parallel number lines.

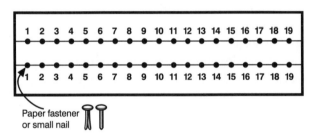

Paper fastener or small nail

Give the children a target number, for example twelve, and ask for all the additions that make this. Place rubber bands on the display to connect the pairs of numbers that make twelve (or draw on the OHT) or let individuals do this. Ask the children:
Where do all of the bands cross? What do you notice?

Repeat for examples such as seventeen, six, nineteen, and so on. In each case, the children should notice that where the bands cross is between the two same numbers that total the given number. So they will cross between the sixes when summing to twelve and between three and a half on each of the number lines when summing to seven.

MAIN ACTIVITY

Whole class, pairs
Show the children the open-topped cube, and ask them to name it or tell them if no-one comes up with an answer. Point out that the faces are squares, but do not take the box apart at this stage. Tell the children that open-topped cubes can be made from squares if the squares are in a suitable arrangement.

Pair the children and give out Resource Sheet 32, scissors and coloured pencils. Say:
The challenge is for you to make an open-topped cube using the squared paper. Drawing, cutting and folding will be necessary.

Give the children time to grapple with the demands of the task. False starts could turn out to be very helpful in getting the children to understand the connection between 3-D objects and nets. When the children have some examples, use your open-topped cube to demonstrate their ideas. Explain that we call the flat drawing a *net*. Now ask the children to draw some nets of open-topped cubes on Resource Sheet 33.

■ Support
Use your open-topped cube with a group to show one way of making a net. Allow the children to copy this way then try to see whether they can find another net to make the open-topped cube.

■ Challenge

Ask the children to test out all of the shapes shown here to see which will make open-topped cubes and which will not.

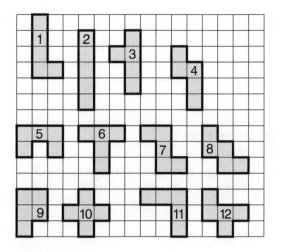

Only numbers 1, 3, 6, 7, 8, 10 and 12 are nets of open-topped cubes.

PLENARY

Using your OHT of Resource Sheet 33, get the children to share nets that they think will make an open-topped cube. As necessary, demonstrate the appropriateness of those suggested, using your open-topped cube.

Key fact or strategy

A variety of nets will fold to make an open-topped cube.

Lesson 3

◢ Learning objectives

Mental/oral starter:
• Recall addition and subtraction facts for each number up to 20

Main activity:
• Recognise directions, and perpendicular and parallel lines

▣ Resources

Photocopies of Resource Sheet 34, supervision for children working around the school, photocopies of Resource Sheet 35, set squares, OHT of Resource Sheet 35, OHT pen

ᵃᵦᶜ Vocabulary

Perpendicular, parallel, right angle, distance

MENTAL/ORAL STARTER

Use this time to give the children a practice test. Suggested items for this are shown here:

3 + 15	12 + 5
7 + 13	2 + 17
9 – 4	19 – 12
20 – 12	11 – 6
8 + 8	6 + 11
20 – 7	8 + 12
11 – 3	15 – 9
8 + 7	17 – 9
6 + 9	9 + 9
15 – 9	2 + 18

MAIN ACTIVITY

Whole class, pairs or small groups

Using drawings of shapes like those shown here explain to the children that a *perpendicular* line is at right angles to another line. Explain that perpendicular does not mean the same as *vertical*. Then explain the term *parallel*.

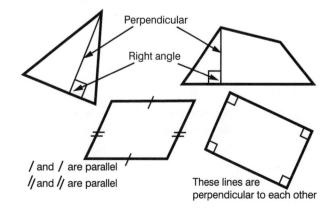

Get the children into pairs or small groups and give them Resource Sheet 34. Ask the children to do the work in the classroom first. When they have done this, use examples from different groups to reinforce the meaning of perpendicular and parallel. Now get the children to find examples around school. When the children have done this, get them to say where they have found any perpendicular or parallel lines. Use the examples to reinforce the meanings of the two terms.

Give out Resource Sheet 35 and ask the children to make notes about the shapes there.

■ **Support**
Draw some shapes with perpendicular lines that are not vertical and get the children to check the right angle using a set square or the corner of a piece of paper.

■ **Challenge**
Ask the children to write an explanation of the difference between *perpendicular* and *vertical*.

PLENARY

Using the OHT of Resource Sheet 35 and ideas from different children, review what is meant by *perpendicular* and *parallel*.

Key fact or strategy

A perpendicular line is at right angles to another line. Perpendicular lines do not have to be vertical or horizontal.

Lesson 4

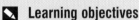

Learning objectives
Mental/oral starter:
• Add/subtract any pair of two-digit numbers, including crossing 100
Main activity:
• Understand and use degrees
• Identify, estimate and order acute and obtuse angles

Resources
Photocopies of Resource Sheets 36 and 37, compasses or dividers

Vocabulary
Angle, right angle, acute, obtuse, estimate, order

MENTAL/ORAL STARTER

By now, the children should be getting very confident in the mental manipulation of common number bonds, so in this session concentrate on the mental methods that they are using to solve problems. Some addition examples to give the children are shown here:
32 + 58
93 + 17
24 + 46
75 + 35
19 + 47

Ways of solving might include summing the units to make ten then summing the tens. Alternatively the children might try summing the tens first. Also they could be using rounding, for example, with 19 + 47 they might do 20 add 47 then take away 1. Give the children time to explain their methods.

MAIN ACTIVITY

Whole class, individuals
Draw some angles on the board (include acute, right and obtuse) and ask the children to tell you anything that they can about them. The children may identify the right angles and then use these in a comparison that is about greater than or less than a right angle. Encourage this response. Then write the terms *acute* and *obtuse* on the board using any comparison with right angles that might have been made. Tell the children:
I am going to give you some angles and I want you to identify them as being acute, obtuse or right angles.

Give out Resource Sheet 36 for the children to work on individually. As they are doing this, encourage them to think about how they might explain what the different terms mean. Then they can complete the final part of the sheet.

Ask the children to share their definitions and correct any misunderstandings at this point. In order to reinforce the ideas, now give the children Resource Sheet 37.

■ Support
Use a pair of compasses or dividers to physically show how a turn might move from being acute to a right angle to greater than a right angle, that is, an obtuse angle.

■ Challenge
Ask the children to draw some angles and label them acute, obtuse or right angle.

PLENARY

Get the children to tell you the examples and answers to Resource Sheet 37. Use this opportunity to review and reinforce the meanings of *right*, *acute* and *obtuse angle*.

Key fact or strategy

Acute angles are less than a right angle (90°) and obtuse angles are greater than a right angle (though less than 180°; the children will meet reflex angles later).

Lesson 5

❏ Learning objectives
Mental/oral starter:
- Add/subtract any pair of two-digit numbers, including crossing 100

Main activity:
- Use a protractor to measure and draw acute and obtuse angles to 5°
- Calculate angles in a straight line

❏ Resources
Set squares and 360° and 180° protractors suitable for use on the OHP, blank OHT and OHT pen, photocopies of Resource Sheet 38, 180° protractors, OHT of Resource Sheet 38, photocopies of Resource Sheet 39, OHT of Resource Sheet 39

❏ Vocabulary
Angle, acute, obtuse, right angle, straight angle, degree, protractor, estimate

MENTAL/ORAL STARTER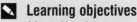

As in the previous lesson, the intention is to get the children explaining how they solve mental computations. Here the concern is with subtraction and a possible set of questions is shown here:

76 – 46
125 – 27
101 – 3
59 – 12
107 –18

The children might use counting back (for example, 101 – 3 could be solved by 101, 100, 99, 98). They might use taking away units, then tens (for example, 76 – 46 could be done this way). Again, they might be employing rounding, for example, 107 – 18 could be done by taking 20 away from 107 to get 87 then adding 2 to get 89. Give the children time to explain their methods.

MAIN ACTIVITY

Whole class, pairs

Put the set squares on the OHP and use them to remind the children of the work that they did last year where they measured some angles using degrees. Review the angles on the set squares so that the children recall 90°, 45°, 60° and 30°. Now place the 360° protractor on the OHP and discuss the fact that there are 360° in a circle. Using this protractor, review the angles that they have just been reminded of.

Now display the 180° protractor and draw a few angles on a blank OHT showing how we can measure these using the protractor. Explain as you do this how to use a protractor (lining up carefully using the base line and the line perpendicular to this). Make the measurements to the nearest 5°.

Tell the children that you want them to try out using protractors but first you want them to make estimates of the degrees in angles that you

27

are going to give them. To do this, they should remember that the smaller the angle the less the number of degrees. If necessary, draw some more angles and measure them to underline this point. Give out Resource Sheet 38 to pairs along with the protractors. Remind the children always to make an estimate before they try using the protractor. When the children have attempted this, display your OHT of Resource Sheet 38 and get the children to help you check solutions, asking for estimates first in each case.

Now use the 360° and the 180° protractors on the OHP to explain that a straight angle must be 180°. Give out Resource Sheet 39 telling the children to work out answers and then check them using their protractors.

■ Support

Work with a protractor on the first two or three questions on Resource Sheet 38.

■ Challenge

Ask the children to draw angles of given amounts, for example 50°, 80°, 35°, 10° and 85°.

PLENARY

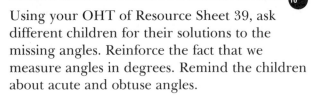

Using your OHT of Resource Sheet 39, ask different children for their solutions to the missing angles. Reinforce the fact that we measure angles in degrees. Remind the children about acute and obtuse angles.

> **Key fact or strategy**
> There are 360° in one complete rotation. A right angle is one quarter of a rotation so that is why it is 90°.

Lesson 6

> ### ◥ Learning objectives
> *Mental/oral starter:*
> • Derive quickly halves of whole numbers 1 to 100
> *Main activity:*
> • Make patterns from rotating shapes
>
> ### ◻ Resources
> Resource Sheet 40 photocopied on two colours of thin card and cut up to make two sets of cards, templates of common 2-D shapes (90, 45, 45 and 90, 60, 30 set squares can be used), plain paper, sharp pencils, protractors, photocopies of Resource Sheet 41, OHT of Resource Sheet 41
>
> ### ▦ Vocabulary
> Rotate, rotation, angle, names of 2-D shapes that you have, protractor

MENTAL/ORAL STARTER

Give two children each a set of the cards made using Resource Sheet 40 and ask them to act as callers. Each child should select a card and call it out in turn. This will make a two-digit number that the class then has to halve. When this has been done as many times as you wish, finish by asking the children:
What is this a half of: 17? … 12.5? … 23 1/2? and so on.

MAIN ACTIVITY

Whole class, pairs

Show the children some of the 2-D shape templates and ask for the names of each of the

shapes. Explain that you are going to give out shape templates and you want the children to draw around them, then turn them however much they choose, keeping one of the corners touching. They should repeat this, turning the same amount each time. An example of template rotation is shown here:

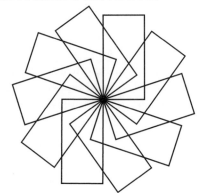

Give out templates and plain paper and make sure that pencils are sharp. Have protractors available if the children ask for these at this stage.

When the children have tried this out with one or more templates, share outcomes and ask:
How much did you turn this one?
What do you think would happen to the pattern if you turned it more? ... less?
Do you get back to where you started?
Can you change the amount of turn to make the shape turn exactly one rotation?

Now give out Resource Sheet 41 and protractors and ask the children to work through the questions there.

■ **Support**
Revise how to measure angle, and that there are 360 degrees in one complete rotation.

■ **Challenge**
Can the children identify those regular polygons that fit exactly into one rotation by using the fact that there are 360 degrees in a circle?

PLENARY

Using your OHT of Resource Sheet 41, get the children to talk through what they have discovered. Emphasise that complete rotations are only possible with some shapes. Collect in the rotating patterns that have been made for display and revision purposes.

Key fact or strategy
The interior angle at the turning vertex of any shape that will rotate exactly in a circle must be a factor of 360 degrees.

Supplementary activities

Mental/oral follow-up

Counting on and back
Using Resource Sheets 27 and 28 get pairs to "test" each other.
Each sheet could be cut up and made into two piles face down.
The children then take it in turns to try and count on or back five
steps. If they counted on the first time, they should count back
the next.

Parallel number lines
Do more work using parallel number lines. Number lines with decimals
or fractions could be developed by the children.

Two-digit additions and subtractions
Get the children to write out two-digit additions or subtractions and all
the ways that they can think of to solve these. Put these on display
and periodically use the examples with the whole class.

Halving
Use the cards made using Resource Sheet 40 to give pairs or small
groups more practice in halving two-digit numbers. These cards can
also be used for other activities such as adding pairs of numbers.

Homework

3-D shapes
If the children have not worked on it, Resource Sheet 31 can be given
to them to complete.

Nets
Give out Resource Sheet 42. Explain to the children that they must ask
permission before taking a box apart.

Development

Shapes in real life
Try to get an architect and a builder in to talk to the children about the
3-D and 2-D shapes that they commonly use in designing and making
buildings. Get the children to find out about famous buildings around
the world. Can they identify some of the shapes in these buildings?

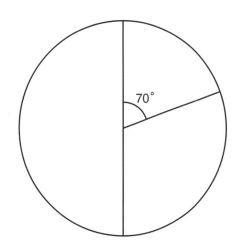

Angles in rotation
Get children to work out angles based on a whole
rotation such as the example shown here. They
should measure and write in the missing angles.

Perpendicular and parallel

Get the children to help you take photographs around the school and the neighbourhood to show perpendicular and parallel lines. These might also be used for work on symmetry, diagonals, horizontal and vertical, and so on. Make an exhibition and invite parents in to view it or make it part of a display in school reception.

Rotating patterns

Give the children more opportunities to make rotating patterns. Use Resource Sheet 43 photocopied on card as a source of templates for the children to use, or have them design their own templates.

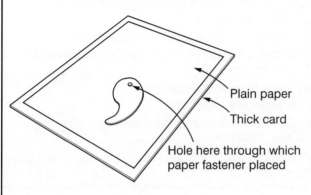

Plain paper

Thick card

Hole here through which paper fastener placed

First lay a plain piece of plain paper over some thick card. Place the template on the paper and make a hole through the template, paper and card. Attach the template with a paper fastener, as shown on the left:

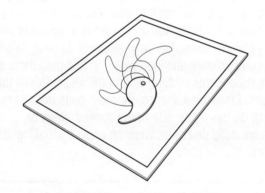

Draw around the template. Rotate it and draw around it again and again.

Get the children to make a collection of logos that display rotation in their pattern.

ICT ideas

Protractor use

"What's my angle?" on *Using ICT to support mathematics in primary schools programs CD-ROM* (DfEE/QCA, 2000) offers an excellent introduction to the use of the protractor for measuring angles. The activity might be used with the whole class on an interactive whiteboard with individual children estimating and then measuring the angles.

Parallel and perpendicular

Can Do Maths Year 5 CD-ROM 3 (Nelson Thornes) includes an activity intended to assess children's ability to recognise parallel and perpendicular lines in 2-D shapes. Children's work is recorded for the teacher and problem areas highlighted.

Unit 4 **Supplementary activities**

Unit 5 Reasoning about shapes

Term				Spring

Framework links

5	8	102–111	Shape and space	Visualise 3-D shapes from 2-D drawings and identify nets of open cube. Recognise directions, and perpendicular and parallel lines. Understand and use degrees. Identify, estimate and order acute and obtuse angles. Use protractor to measure and draw acute and obtuse angles to 5˚. Make patterns from rotating shapes. Calculate angles in a straight line.
		76–81	Reasoning about shapes	Recognise and explain patterns and relationships, generalise and predict.

Setting the scene	By now, the children should be confidently naming common 2-D and 3-D shapes and be able to explain and use some of their key characteristics. Exploring shapes, their names, relationships and patterns in space is an important way of getting children to explore mathematical thinking. Work done on shape informs number work and vice versa. In this unit, there are two sets of ideas. The first concerns rectangles and the ability to see this shape in different contexts. Embedded shapes are often quite difficult to perceive but being able to do this helps with many applied areas of mathematics. Secondly, we build on recent work on angle by looking at the angle of a straight line.
Starting points	The children should know the names and main characteristics of 2-D shapes. They should know about the use of degrees in the measurement of angle.
Checking progress	■ All children should know the characteristics of a rectangle and understand the idea of angle. ■ Children requiring additional support will need help in visualising shapes that are embedded. They may also need more work on the use of the protractor. ■ Some children will have progressed further and will readily see that rectangles can be of different size and orientation in a figure. They will also be confident in measuring angle.

Lesson 1

✎ Learning objectives
Mental/oral starter:
- Know by heart multiplication facts up to 10 × 10
- Derive quickly division facts corresponding to tables up to 10 × 10

Main activity:
- Recognise and explain patterns and relationships, generalise and predict

📖 Resources
OHT or large drawing of A from Resource Sheet 44, photocopies of Resource Sheet 44, coloured pens or pencils, General Resource Sheet B

🔤 Vocabulary
Square, rectangle, angle, degrees, calculate

MENTAL/ORAL STARTER

Write some numbers on the board that are products in the tables that the children should now know, for example 35, 56, 18, 90, 25, 36 and 27. In turn, ask what each of these numbers can be divided by. Then ask for the multiplication that relates to this. Repeat with further numbers suggested by the class.

MAIN ACTIVITY

Whole class, individuals, pairs

Using the OHT or drawing of A from Resource Sheet 44, ask the children to help you work out how many rectangles the drawing actually contains. There are nine, as shown here:

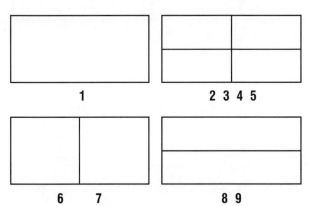

Give out Resource Sheet 44 and ask the children individually to check that this is correct. Encourage the children to think of different ways to keep a record. Now ask them to try to work out the rectangles in B and C, working with a friend.

■ Support
Make several copies of the resource sheet diagrams so that each rectangle can be cut out if necessary.

■ Challenge
Following on from A and B on Resource Sheet 44, can the children extend the two-row pattern to another column and work out the number of rectangles? They could use General Resource Sheet B to draw their rectangle patterns.

PLENARY

Ask different pairs about B then C on Resource Sheet 44. Is there agreement in the class? Work through each as appropriate, cutting up if necessary.

> **Key fact or strategy**
> To solve puzzles like these, it is necessary to be methodical and use well-organised and clear recording.

Lesson 2

 Learning objectives
Mental/oral starter:
• Know by heart multiplication facts up to 10 x 10
Main activity:
• Recognise and explain patterns and relationships, generalise and predict

Resources
Board protractor or one that you can use on OHP with a blank OHT and OHT pen, protractors, photocopies of Resource Sheet 45, millimetre rulers, sharp pencils, OHT of Resource Sheet 45

Vocabulary
Angle, degrees, statement

MENTAL/ORAL STARTER

Concentrate in this session on the learning of the ×7 table. Start by asking for the answers to seven times in the ×2, ×3, ×4, ×5 and ×10 tables. With the help of the children, now write out the full ×7 table up to 7 × 10. Get the whole class to read this through with you. Ask the children to work on the table at home.

MAIN ACTIVITY

Whole class, individuals

The children have already done work on the concepts in this lesson. Use this session as a revision/test to find out what they know. Ask the children to describe how to use a protractor, demonstrating on the OHP or the board. Draw angles to try out their suggestions.

Tell the children that in this lesson they are going to need to use protractors to measure some angles accurately and they will also need to sum angles. Give out Resource Sheet 45 to everyone together with protractors and rulers. Check that pencils are sharp; then let the children tackle the questions.

▪ Support

Draw some more angles and get individuals to measure these while you observe them.

▪ Challenge

Ask the children to create a set of single angles which will form a straight line when paired.

PLENARY

Take in the resource sheets for scrutiny, before conducting the plenary session.

Using your OHT of Resource Sheet 45, get different children to tell you the measured angles so that you can write them in. Ask:

What do the angles total in each case?

Write a general statement of the type "The angles on a straight line add up to 180 degrees", under the direction of the children.

Key fact or strategy
Placing the protractor in the appropriate starting position is crucial to success.

Supplementary activities

Mental/oral follow-up

Tables
Continue with five-minute repetitions of all the multiplication tables. Get the children to continue exploring patterns in the products of particular tables.

Homework

Tables
Give particular multiplication tables to practice at home. Follow this up with short rehearsals in school.

Development

Rectangles
Extend the rectangle work from Lesson 1 (page 33) by increasing number of columns or rows.

Degrees
Develop statements about the number of degrees in a right angle and a circle.

Pie charts
Link the work on the circle with pie charts in newspapers and magazines.

ICT ideas

Shape challenges
The "Shape it up" section of the Cadbury Learning Zone includes two shape challenges which can be used as support activities:

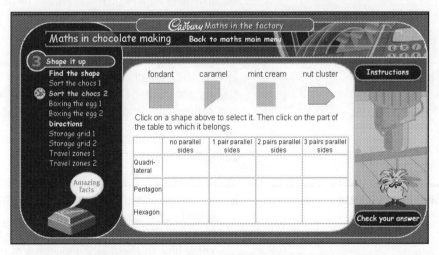

- "Sort the chocs" in which children have to sort all the different chocolate shapes for a special order

- "Boxing the egg" in which the children have to identify different nets that will make chocolate boxes.

Find these challenges at www.cadburylearningzone.co.uk

Puzzles and games
Zoombinis Maths Journey (Learning Company) includes a range of maths puzzles at four levels of difficulty. The package also includes some printable games and activities.

Unit 6 Measures

Term				Spring

Framework links

7–8	10	86–101	Measures including problems	Understand area measured in square centimetres. Use formula in words for area of rectangle. Use, read and write standard metric units of mass, abbreviations. Know relationships between them. Convert larger to smaller units of mass. Suggest suitable units and equipment to estimate or measure mass. Read measurements from scales.
				Use all four operations to solve measurement word problems. Choose appropriate operations/calculation methods. Explain working.
		112–117	Handling data	Represent and interpret data in a line graph (e.g. weight of a baby at monthly intervals from birth to one year). Recognise when points can be joined to show trends.

Setting the scene

In this unit, the children are working on the concept of area and metric measures of mass. The children are presented with the opportunity to further their knowledge of area, learning that it can be measured in square centimetres and that length multiplied by breadth gives us the area of a rectangle. The children should also come to have confidence in their own understanding of standard metric measures of mass and the abbreviations kg and g. The children will be able to confirm that they know common fractions of a kilogram and can convert kilograms to grams and grams to kilograms.

Starting points

In Year 4/P5, the children counted squares to find the areas of simple shapes and learned that area is a "square" measure taking account of the two dimensions, length and breadth, at one time.

They also worked on the association between grams and kilograms and common fractions of a kilogram.

Checking progress

- All children should be able to demonstrate that they know what area is and that it can be measured in square centimetres, and they should be able to describe how to find the area of a rectangle. They should know how to use metric measures of mass and their abbreviations, convert kilograms to grams and read measurements of mass from scales.
- Children requiring additional support will benefit from extra practice in working on finding areas by counting squares and calculation and in estimating and weighing masses.
- Some children will have progressed further and be adept at finding areas of rectangles using length x breadth, finding dimensions of rectangles when given the area and length of one side, and estimating and weighing.

Lesson 1

Learning objectives
Mental/oral starter:
• Convert metres to centimetres
Main activity:
• Understand area measured in square centimetres
• Use counting methods and calculation to find the areas of rectangles
• Estimate and measure areas

Resources
OHT of Resource Sheet 46, OHT pen, photocopies of Resource Sheet 46, area measuring task boxes (see Main activity for instructions), rulers or measuring tapes, photocopies of Resource Sheet 47

Vocabulary
Metre, centimetre, convert, area, cm², rectangle, length, breadth, estimate

MENTAL/ORAL STARTER

Write up a list of measurements in metres on the board. Invite individual children in turn to convert them into centimetres. Here is a suggested list:
6 m
10 m
130 m
500 m
7.2 m
63.8 m
5.55 m

Discuss how the answers can be checked using a calculator. Allow a child to check each one in turn.

Then write up a new list of measures in centimetres for the children to convert into metres. Here are some suggestions:
3 000 cm
50 000 cm
500 cm
42 cm
176 cm
7.5 cm
10.10 cm

MAIN ACTIVITY

Whole class, individuals, small groups

Show the children the OHT of Resource Sheet 46. Tell them that the squares on the grid are centimetre squares. Invite children in turn to count the squares to find the areas of the rectangles. Remind the children that we write area in centimetres as *square centimetres (cm²).*

Then look at rectangle A with the children again. Ask:
What is the length of the longer side?
What is the length of the shorter side?

Then show the children that if we multiply the length of the longer side (length) by the length of the shorter side (breadth), the answer is the area of the rectangle. Tell the children that this way of finding area works for rectangles. Calculate the areas of rectangles B, C, D, E and F, using this method.

To follow up this work, give each child a copy of Resource Sheet 46 so they can count and calculate the areas of the rectangles for themselves. Before they begin, show the children that you have set up a box of area measuring tasks for each work group, and they should attempt these as a group when they have finished working on Resource Sheet 46.

Before the lesson, collect five rectangular items in a box for each group. These items should be marked up carefully so that the children know which surface to measure. The children will be required to estimate and measure the area of each item using tapes or rulers. Each box could contain items such as a rectangle of card, a notebook, a register, a large postage stamp, a wooden box, a video case or a comic. Children should make their own record of the group work on Resource Sheet 47.

■ Support

Following the demonstration, check that these children know that they are counting and then calculating areas, and how this is done.

■ **Challenge**

Have some reserve items ready so that children can estimate and measure their areas.

PLENARY

Check, compare and discuss the work the children have done on Resource Sheet 47.

Key fact or strategy

Area can be measured in square centimetres (cm²) and can be calculated for rectangles using the lengths of the sides.

Lesson 2

Learning objectives

Mental/oral starter:
• Order a given set of positive and negative integers
Main activity:
• Understand area measured in square centimetres (cm²)
• Use formula in words for area of rectangle

Resources

A string across the room or board, Resource Sheets 48 and 49 photocopied on card and cut up, pegs, bulldog clips or large paper clips, area workbook made from Resource Sheets 50 to 53 (see Main activity for instructions), scissors, centimetre rulers, Resource Sheet 54 photocopied on thin card and cut out

Vocabulary

Metre, centimetre, area, cm², rectangle, length, breadth, drawn to scale, estimate

MENTAL/ORAL STARTER

Hand out the positive number cards from Resource Sheet 48 one at a time and allow the children to attach them at a point along the line where they think they will fit. It is the convention that the lowest number goes at the left-hand end of the line, when looking at it from the children's point of view.

Then take these cards down and work on the negative numbers from Resource Sheet 49, or extend the line towards the left so that the negative numbers can be hung up too. If the cards are used before the time for the activity is over, call out numbers and ask children to point to where they would fit on the line.

Make additional cards that focus on the range of digits with which the children seem to have difficulty. Thus, for example, focusing on positive numbers, additional cards with four digits can be created to give children practice in working with thousands.

MAIN ACTIVITY

Whole class, individuals

Before the lesson, photocopy Resource Sheets 50 to 53 to make up the area workbook. Sheet 51 should be photocopied on the back of 50, and 53 on the back of 52. You can then cut

them out and assemble the booklets before the start of the lesson. Show the children a made-up copy of the area workbook and talk through the activities they are going to be asked to do. Ask them to leave the definition on the cover until they have completed the book. Children should be given their own copy to complete.

■ **Support**

Visit these children and offer them the clue cards from Resource Sheet 54 and additional explanation as necessary. You may need several copies of the clue cards.

■ **Challenge**

These children can create their own definition of area and then look in mathematical and other dictionaries to find and compare the definitions there with their own.

PLENARY

Look at the parts of the booklet which the children found difficult and discuss these with the class.

Key fact or strategy

Area can be measured in square centimetres (cm²) and can be calculated for rectangles using the lengths of the sides.

Lesson 3

Learning objectives
Mental/oral starter:
- Order a set of fractions

Main activity:
- Know common fractions of a kilogram
- Convert larger to smaller units of mass
- Round masses to the nearest kilogram

Resources
Items to be weighed (e.g. sealed bags of pulses or rice or parcels made up to given weights) including one that weighs 1 kg, kitchen balance, electronic balance, photocopies of Resource Sheets 55 and 56, plain paper

Vocabulary
Kilogram (kg), gram (g), fraction, convert, rounding, nearest

MENTAL/ORAL STARTER

Use this time to inspect, compare and discuss common fractions. These are the fractions which should be included:

$\frac{1}{4}$ $\frac{1}{2}$ $\frac{3}{4}$ $\frac{1}{10}$ $\frac{1}{100}$

You can add $\frac{1}{3}$, $\frac{2}{3}$ and $\frac{1}{6}$ and any other fractions in everyday use in class.

Write two fractions on the board. For each, discuss how many make one whole, which is the larger, and how we can determine this.

MAIN ACTIVITY

Whole class, individuals

Show the children the pack or parcel that weighs one kilogram. Ask them to pass it around and say how much they think it weighs. Weigh it on one of the balances in front of the children.

Then repeat this procedure with the other packs or parcels, so that the children have the experience of the "feel" of different masses. This will support their understanding of comparisons of mass and their estimating skills.

Talk about how many grams there are in one kilogram, and then write on the board the numbers of grams in common fractions of a kilogram. Practise converting 1 kg and 0.5 kg into grams, and 1 000 g and 150 g into kilograms. Rub this off the board and hand out Resource Sheet 55 to the children.

When they have had ten minutes to work on the sheet, call the class together and ask them what is meant by *approximation* and *rounding*. Round

1.2 kg to 1 kg and 1.6 kg to 2 kg on the board. Then set down Resource Sheet 56 for the children to take when they complete Resource Sheet 55.

Support
Offer these children the reminder that there are 1 000 g in 1 kg. They can examine the parcels again in a discussion of fractions and decimal fractions. For example, say:
If a parcel weighs 250 g, I need four parcels to make 1 kg, so each parcel is $\frac{1}{4}$ kg or 0.25 kg.

Challenge
If the children complete Resource Sheets 55 and 56, they can create a new worksheet of their own on plain paper, offering the opportunity for children to round masses to the nearest kg. These sheets can be added to class resources, or typed up so that they can be offered as homework. (It is important to give credit to the author so the sheet should carry the line: "Written by _____ Class _____ Date _____ and distributed with their permission.")

PLENARY

Try out more rounding and conversion from kilograms to grams and grams to kilograms orally with the class.

Key fact or strategy

Grams can be converted to kilograms (and kilograms to grams) by dividing (multiplying) by 1 000.

Lesson 4

✎ Learning objectives
Mental/oral starter:
- Convert kilograms to grams

Main activity:
- Suggest suitable equipment to estimate or measure mass
- Read measurements from scales

📖 Resources
Sets of parcels (see Main activity for instructions), collection of weighing instruments calibrated in g such as bathroom scales, pan balances, kitchen balance, electronic scales, letter scales, spring balances, photocopies of Resource Sheets 57 and 58

ᵃᵇᶜ Vocabulary
Estimate, measure, kg, g, scales, reading, mass

MENTAL/ORAL STARTER

Write on the board the following column of numbers of kilograms:

1 kg
2 kg
5 kg
10 kg
100 kg

With the children's help, next to this column, write the number of grams in each of these, thus:

1000 g
2000 g
5000 g
10000 g
100000 g

Using this comparison/conversion chart, the children can now respond individually to the challenge of converting kilograms to grams. Here are some possible challenges:

3 kg
6 kg
2.5 kg
10.25 kg
100.1 kg

MAIN ACTIVITY

Whole class, pairs or small groups, individuals

Before the lesson, make up a set of seven parcels of different masses. Number the parcels 1 to 7. If possible, replicate this set of masses, so that there are plenty for the children to have access to.

Display and discuss the weighing instruments with the class and talk about what they do. Allow the children access to a balance, either in a small group or preferably in pairs. They can take the parcels in any order, estimate their masses, and then weigh them on their balance. All children should record the outcomes on a copy of Resource Sheet 57.

■ Support
Give these children practical help in getting their estimates recorded before weighing, checking the balance and ensuring an accurate reading of the scales.

■ Challenge
When the weighing is done, the children can be looking in pairs at Resource Sheet 58, ready for the Plenary.

PLENARY

Hand out copies of Resource Sheet 58 and discuss with the children their ideas about the equipment to use in each case. Allow them to take the resource sheet home to complete (see Homework, page 41).

Key fact or strategy
We choose appropriate equipment for weighing jobs.

Supplementary activities

Mental/oral follow-up

Money conversion
Write some sums of money in pounds on the board and ask the children to convert them to pence.

Homework

Weighing equipment
Ask the children to complete Resource Sheet 58 at home.

Development

Weighing practice
Give the children more practice in weighing and using scales. They could find ways of tabulating their results.

Area plans
Collect catalogues which have kitchen and bathroom layouts from do-it-yourself shops. Show the children how the area of each cupboard and worktop can be calculated and set down on the plan to show if the layout is practical and roomy.

Wallpaper area
Help the children to calculate the area of a classroom wall. Obtain a full roll of wallpaper, which gives its dimensions on it. Invite children to work out how many pieces of paper of what dimensions would be required for the wall.

ICT ideas

Area and perimeter
*Maths Explorer: Shape and Space (*Granada Learning) is based around the theme of a medieval castle and includes activities relating to all of the standard metric units covered this year as well as work on area and perimeter. Work is set at three ability levels with children having to measure the area and perimeter of the "Queen's banners".
The CD-ROM also includes a narrated full-picture slide show about the maths concepts needed to complete the investigation.

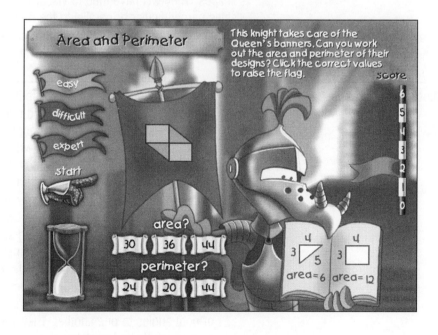

Unit 7 Shape and space

Term   Summer

Framework links

8–10	15	102–111	Shape and space	Recognise reflective symmetry in regular polygons. Complete symmetrical patterns with two lines of symmetry at right angles. Reflect shapes in mirror parallel to one side. Recognise where shape will be after translation.
		76–81	Reasoning about shapes	Make and investigate a general statement about shapes.
		86–101	Measures including problems	Use timetables. Know and use relationship between units of time. Use, read and write standard metric units of capacity, including abbreviations and pint, gallon. Know and use relationships between them. Convert larger to smaller units of capacity, including gallons to pints. Suggest suitable units and equipment to estimate or measure capacity. Read measurements from scales. Use all four operations to solve measurement word problems, including time. Choose appropriate operations/calculation methods. Explain working.

Setting the scene

It is only by repeatedly trying out and thinking about what happens behind a mirror line that the children will be able to produce descriptions, drawings and explanations of reflections unerringly. Here they are given the opportunity to explore and detect reflective symmetry in regular polygons. They move on to create complex symmetrical patterns where there are two mirror lines at right angles to one another and visualise the reflections of shapes which lie parallel to a mirror on one side. The final lesson introduces the children to the idea of translation.

Starting points

In Year 4/P5, the children will have begun to look at lines of symmetry in shapes. They will have tried to visualise reflections of shapes that have all sides perpendicular or parallel to the mirror line. They will also have made patterns by translating shapes. In the autumn and spring terms of this year, they have looked for lines of symmetry in triangles.

Checking progress

- All children should be able to describe and demonstrate reflective symmetry in regular polygons and make patterns with two lines of symmetry at right angles to one another. They should know how to reflect simple shapes in a mirror where not all sides are perpendicular or parallel to the mirror. They should attempt to plot co-ordinates.
- Children requiring additional support will benefit from extra practice in finding out how many lines of symmetry there are in regular polygons, completing patterns with two lines of symmetry at right angles to one another and reflecting shapes in a mirror. They may also need more work on making translation patterns.
- Some children will have progressed further and be adept at describing how to determine the number of lines of symmetry in a regular polygon and creating patterns with two lines of symmetry at right angles to one another. They will be able to identify the co-ordinates of a translated shape.

Lesson 1

✎ Learning objectives
Mental/oral starter:
- Express simple fractions as percentages

Main activity:
- Recognise reflective symmetry in regular polygons
- Know how to determine the number of lines of symmetry in a regular polygon

📖 Resources
Resource Sheet 59 photocopied on thin card and cut out, board rule or metre stick, photocopies of Resource Sheets 60 and 61, rulers, scissors, photocopies of Resource Sheet 62

🔤 Vocabulary
Axes of reflective symmetry, regular, polygon, line of symmetry

MENTAL/ORAL STARTER

Hand out the fraction cards made from Resource Sheet 59 to individual children. Then hold up the percentage cards in turn. The child holding the matching percentage card should call out "Match!" and hold up the card. The whole class views the card and checks the match.

When all the fraction cards have been exhausted, take in the percentage cards. Shuffle both sets, and then hand out the fraction cards, before repeating the game. Then take in the fraction cards and shuffle both sets again. Finish by holding up cards at random, asking the children to give the matching fraction or percentage each time.

MAIN ACTIVITY

Whole class, individuals, pairs

Draw a regular hexagon on the board and alongside it an irregular polygon with six sides. Revise what *polygon* and *regular* mean, using the diagrams on the board. Establish that the children know that a polygon is any plane shape and that a regular polygon has all sides of the same length (and therefore all internal angles are equal).

Using the board rule or metre stick, discuss whether the two shapes show reflective symmetry. The irregular hexagon may or may not show reflective symmetry, but the regular hexagon will show symmetry with six *axes of symmetry*.

Tell the children that they are going to be looking carefully at irregular and regular polygons, and trying to determine which show reflective symmetry. In those that show

symmetry, they should try to find out how many axes of symmetry there are.

Give each child a copy of Resource Sheets 60 and 61 along with a ruler and a pair of scissors. They should cut out and fold the shapes, or place their rule across them to try to determine whether the shapes show reflective symmetry.

When they have experimented with all the shapes they should try to complete the chart on Resource Sheet 62.

▪ Support
Visit these children frequently, showing them how to make folds across the shapes in different directions in order to check out whether they show reflective symmetry.

▪ Challenge
These children can talk to a partner about how they determine the number of axes of symmetry in a regular polygon.

PLENARY

Look at the regular polygons again with the children, and for each polygon ask how many axes of symmetry there are. Begin with the equilateral triangle, then a square, pentagon, hexagon and heptagon. The children should all note that the numbers of axes of symmetry matches the number of sides in each shape.

> **Key fact or strategy**
> Regular polygons display reflective symmetry.

43

Lesson 2

◆ Learning objectives
Mental/oral starter:
- Relate fractions to their decimal representations

Main activity:
- Reflect shapes in a mirror line parallel to one side

▣ Resources
Blank OHT, OHT pen and cloth (optional), board rule or metre stick, photocopies of Resource Sheets 63 and 64, rulers, plane safety mirrors

ᵃᵇᶜ Vocabulary
Reflection, 2-D shape, side, mirror line, parallel, perpendicular

MENTAL/ORAL STARTER

Draw this chart across the board and write in the top row of fractions:

$\frac{1}{10}$	$\frac{1}{8}$	$\frac{1}{5}$	$\frac{1}{4}$	$\frac{3}{10}$	$\frac{1}{3}$	$\frac{3}{8}$	$\frac{2}{5}$	$\frac{1}{2}$	$\frac{3}{5}$	$\frac{5}{8}$	$\frac{2}{3}$	$\frac{7}{10}$	$\frac{3}{4}$	$\frac{4}{5}$	$\frac{7}{8}$	$\frac{9}{10}$
0.1	0.125	0.2	0.25	0.3	0.33	0.375	0.4	0.5	0.6	0.625	0.66	0.7	0.75	0.8	0.875	0.9

Ask children in turn to write up each fraction as a decimal fraction. When the chart is complete, rub out the top row and ask individuals to say what each fraction matching a decimal fraction is.

If you wish, this chart can be written on an OHT with the children's help.

MAIN ACTIVITY

Whole class, individuals, pairs

Using a board rule or metre stick, draw a rhombus or kite shape on the board and alongside it a mirror line, as shown here:

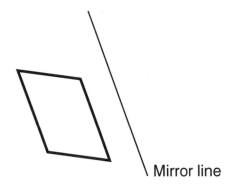

Mirror line

Make sure that the mirror line is parallel to one of the sides of the shape. As a response to the children's suggestions, draw in the reflection of the shape, pointing out that it appears as far behind the mirror line as the shape is in front and in the same orientation to the mirror. The reflection should look something like this:

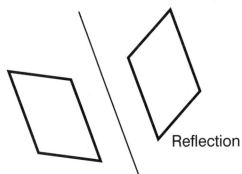

Reflection

Try this same exercise once or twice more, each time choosing a shape with at least one straight side that can be placed parallel to the mirror line. Then give the children each a copy of Resource Sheet 63 and a ruler to try their own hand at drawing reflections. When they finish, they can compare their work with that of a partner. Do not give the children access to plane safety mirrors at this stage.

Then the children should try to draw the reflections on Resource Sheet 64 where the mirror line is drawn at an angle to the edge of the page. This tests whether the children are able to align the shape and its image in relation to the mirror line.

■ Support
Allow these children to view the reflection in a plane safety mirror before putting the mirror aside and drawing the reflection.

■ **Challenge**

These children can draw their own mirror line on paper and create shapes which they can "reflect".

PLENARY

Discuss the problems the children met in completing the resource sheets. Show them how to fold the sheet along the mirror line before holding it up to the light to check the accuracy of their drawings. They can also test out their work using the plane safety mirrors.

> **Key fact or strategy**
> The reflection of a shape lying parallel to a mirror line is the same distance behind the mirror line as the shape is in front, and lies parallel to the mirror line.

Lesson 3

◣ Learning objectives
Mental/oral starter:
• Derive quickly two-digit pairs of numbers that total 100
Main activity:
• Complete symmetrical patterns with two lines of symmetry at right angles

◧ Resources
Resource Sheets 65 and 66 photocopied on thin card and cut out, box, OHT of General Resource Sheet D, OHT pen and cloth, photocopies of Resource Sheets 67 and 68, OHTs of Resource Sheets 67 and 68

ᵃᵇᶜ Vocabulary
Symmetrical pattern, grid, quadrant, line of symmetry, right angle, reflection

MENTAL/ORAL STARTER

Place all the two-digit number cards made from Resource Sheet 65 in a box. Hand each child a game card made from Resource Sheet 66. Pick up, show and call out two-digit numbers in turn. The children mark their card if they have a number which, with the number on display, will sum to 100. When their card is full, they call "Full house!" The cards have been created so that the children can take note of number pairs in a pattern.

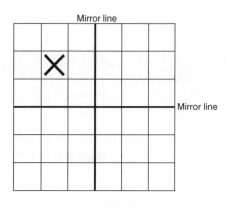

MAIN ACTIVITY

Whole class, individuals

Once two lines of symmetry at right angles are introduced into pattern-making, the concept begins to get tricky. The children will need help in looking at each element in a pattern, and working out where all the reflections of that element are going to appear before going on to the next element. Using an OHT of General Resource Sheet D, place just one simple shape in the grid, as shown here:

Then draw in its reflections:

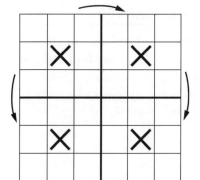

Rub these out, then draw two shapes in one quadrant and reflect them, for example:

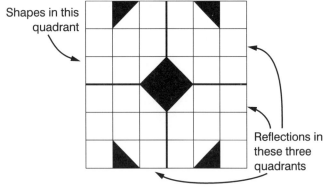

Shapes in this quadrant

Reflections in these three quadrants

Finally draw shapes in all four quadrants and reflect them:

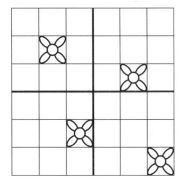

Give the children each a copy of Resource Sheet 67 to try to complete.

■ **Support**

Allow these children to talk through the patterns made in the introduction again, before tackling those on Resource Sheet 67.

■ **Challenge**

Those who work quickly can try the reflections of the shapes on Resource Sheet 68 and then draw their own patterns to reflect in the second symmetry grid B.

PLENARY

Show the children the OHTs of Resource Sheets 67 and 68, working through them to produce the resulting reflection patterns.

Key fact or strategy

Pattern-making can employ two lines of symmetry at right angles.

Lesson 4

Learning objectives

Mental/oral starter:
• Derive quickly all pairs of multiples of 50 with a total of 1 000
Main activity:
• Recognise where a shape will be after translation

Resources

OHT of General Resource Sheet B, OHT pens, photocopies of Resource Sheets 69 and 70, photocopy Resource Sheet 69 on thin card and cut out the shapes several times, box

Vocabulary

Shape, grid, axes, co-ordinates, translation

MENTAL/ORAL STARTER

With the children's help, work out all the multiples of 50 from zero to 1 000 and write a list on the board. Then, again with the children's help, write up pairs of numbers from the list which sum to 1 000, thus:

0   + 1 000
50   + 950
100 + 900
150 + 850

200 + 800
250 + 750
300 + 700
350 + 650
400 + 600
450 + 550
500 + 500

Then rub out some of these numbers and ask children in turn to supply the missing number.

MAIN ACTIVITY

Whole class, individuals, pairs

Using the OHT of General Resource Sheet B, draw in two axes and label them with co-ordinates. Then draw a simple shape such as a rectangle in the grid. Talk about moving the rectangle in the grid without turning it. Point out that the rectangle stays the same shape and size. Draw in the rectangle in some new positions, showing how many units to the left or right, or up or down it has been moved. Confirm that when we move a shape in this way the action is called *translation*.

Give children a copy of Resource Sheet 69 for them to try their own translation of shapes. Resource Sheet 70 is for those who complete Resource Sheet 69.

■ Support

Before the lesson, put several sets of card shapes cut from Resource Sheet 69 in an open box. Allow children needing support access to the box of shapes. They can place the relevant shape on the grid and physically move it to find where it goes.

■ Challenge

These children should share the work they have done on Resource Sheet 70 with a partner, discussing discrepancies in their work.

PLENARY

Address all the difficulties the children say they had, and show the children model answers and explain how they were arrived at.

> **Key fact or strategy**
> Shapes can be visualised after translation (change in location without turning)

Lesson 5

> ### Learning objectives
> *Mental/oral starter:*
> * Partition to multiply by 2 or 3
> *Main activity:*
> * Know what a diagonal is
> * Draw diagonals in on polygons
>
> ### Resources
> Photocopies of Resource Sheets 71 and 72, rulers, rough paper
>
> ### Vocabulary
> Diagonal, polygon

MENTAL/ORAL STARTER

Generate a list of ten 2-digit numbers, ten 3-digit numbers and ten 4-digit numbers. Take each of these numbers in turn and invite the children to multiply them by two. Discuss the methods they use to do these multiplications in their heads. Point out that one way to double a number is to double the units, the tens, the hundreds and the thousands and then add these numbers together.

Then invite the children to multiply the numbers by three. Again, discuss their methods. If there is time, create a new list of numbers and repeat the ×2 and the ×3 multiplication.

MAIN ACTIVITY

Whole class, individuals

Ask the children what they understand by the word *diagonal*. Draw a polygon on the board. Draw in all the diagonals, showing that a diagonal joins any corner (*vertex*) with any non-adjacent vertex. The children have the opportunity to demonstrate that they understand this by drawing in the diagonals on the shapes on Resource Sheets 71 and 72.

■ Support

Draw polygons on rough paper on which the children can draw in diagonals while you look on. When they recognise where all the diagonals go in a shape, allow them to complete the resource sheets.

■ Challenge

Give these children rough paper on which they should draw shapes with nine and ten sides, and then see how many diagonals these shapes have.

PLENARY

Confirm what the children have learned by drawing polygons on the board and asking them to work out how many diagonals there will be before they are drawn in. Confirm that a triangle does not have diagonals.

> **Key fact or strategy**
> A diagonal of a polygon is a line joining any vertex to any non-adjacent vertex.

Supplementary activities

Mental/oral follow-up

Two-digit number game
As a follow-up to the number game in Lesson 3 (page 45), more random game cards can be made using General Resource Sheet E. Along with the two-digit cards made up from Resource Sheet 65, the game can be played again.

Decimal pairs
Give the children whiteboards and a 60-second time limit. How many pairs of decimals that sum to one can they find? Then play the game again asking the children to find pairs of decimals that sum to ten.

Multiplying by five and ten
Use random number lists (two-, three- and four-digit numbers) to work out methods for multiplying by five and ten orally.

Tests of divisibility
Check out and list the tests of divisibility that the children know (for example numbers ending in 5 or 0 can be divided by five). Use them to carry through divisions.

Homework

Symmetry
Give out General Resource Sheet B and ask children to draw the following there:
• two shapes which are irregular and do not show reflective symmetry
• a shape which is irregular but shows reflective symmetry
• two regular polygons which have more than three axes of symmetry.

Development

Symmetry grids
Give out two copies of General Resource Sheet D to each child. Ask them to use one axis of symmetry across one grid, and colour a pattern of squares that is symmetrical. On the second grid, they should use the two axes at right angles to one another and then make a colour pattern that conforms to the two axes of symmetry.

Symmetry in art
Look for patterns with one, two or more axes of symmetry in the art and artefacts from a range of different cultures. Here are some examples:
• the world of Islam
• ancient civilisations, such as the Greeks, Romans or Egyptians
• the Aztecs
• Native Americans.

Translations in real life
Investigate translation of shapes in the school and local environment. For example, translation of shape is used in building construction and decoration, and wall and fence construction.

Unit 7 **Supplementary activities**

ICT ideas

Angle and symmetry

"VersaTile" on *Using ICT to support mathematics in primary schools programs CD-ROM* (DfEE/QCA, 2000) gives children the opportunity to predict and hypothesise when working with angle, rotational and line symmetry, translation and area through the use and development of tiling patterns. It is an ideal tool for drawing and manipulating tiles and fits in well with the Year 5 objective that children should "use a computer program to create a 'tile' and use it by alternately translating the tile and its reflection along a line".

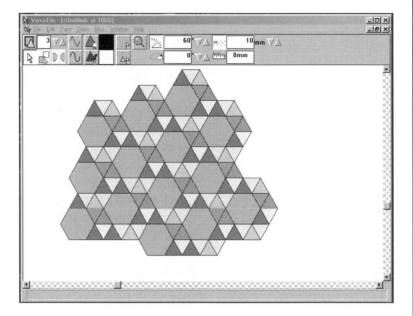

Unit 8   Reasoning about shapes

Term				Summer	

Framework links

8–10	15	102–111	Shape and space	Recognise reflective symmetry in regular polygons. Complete symmetrical patterns with two lines of symmetry at right angles. Reflect shapes in mirror parallel to one side. Recognise where shape will be after translation.
		76–81	Reasoning about shapes	Make and investigate a general statement about shapes.
		86–101	Measures including problems	Use timetables. Know and use relationship between units of time. Use, read and write standard metric units of capacity, including abbreviations and pint, gallon. Know and use relationships between them. Convert larger to smaller units of capacity, including gallons to pints. Suggest suitable units and equipment to estimate or measure capacity. Read measurements from scales. Use all four operations to solve measurement word problems, including time. Choose appropriate operations/calculation methods. Explain working.

Setting the scene

In this unit, the children are considering propositions about shapes. They do this in respect of earlier work on perimeter, and in relation to patterns of squares. To explore the ideas here, the children will need to be clear and logical about measuring and calculating and about rules for combining shapes.

Starting points

The children should know what perimeter is and what measurements are needed to calculate perimeter. They have had experiences of defining and following rules in other units.

Checking progress

- All children should be able to explain perimeter. They should be able to calculate perimeter through the addition of lengths.
- Children requiring additional support will need help in formulating general statements. They may also need help with identifying duplicates of shapes.
- Some children will have progressed further and will readily appreciate general statements about shapes. They will be confident in developing sets of related composite shapes avoiding duplication.

Lesson 1

> ### Learning objectives
> *Mental/oral starter:*
> • Partition to multiply by 5 and by 10
> *Main activity:*
> • Make and investigate a general statement about shapes
>
> ### Resources
> Photocopies of Resource Sheet 73, rulers
>
> ### Vocabulary
> Perimeter, regular, equilateral, triangle, square, pentagon, hexagon, octagon, polygon

MENTAL/ORAL STARTER

Remind the children what *partitioning* means. Get individuals to suggest a few examples of two-digit numbers and then partition them to reinforce understanding. Take some of the suggested numbers and ask the class to use partitioning to multiply these numbers by ten and then by five and then compose final answers. Look at the relationship between these two sets of answers.

MAIN ACTIVITY

Whole class, individuals

Ask:
What does perimeter *mean?*
What does regular *mean when we are talking about shapes?*

Tell the children that they are going to be measuring some regular shapes in order to work out perimeters. Give out Resource Sheet 73 and rulers. Tell the children to work out the perimeter of each of the shapes on the sheet using measurement and any calculations that they choose.

■ Support

Work through the first shape on the sheet if necessary. Calculate the perimeter through measurement and addition at this stage.

■ Challenge

Ask the children to write a sentence to explain to someone else how to calculate the perimeter of a given regular polygon.

PLENARY

Get the children to share their results. Do they all agree? Ask individuals how they worked out the perimeter for each shape. With the help of the class, write a general statement about calculating the perimeter of any regular polygon. Ask the children to write down their own copy of this statement. It should take the form "The perimeter of a regular 2-D shape (polygon) is the length of a side multiplied by the number of sides".

> **Key fact or strategy**
> It is important to put processes into words and this should always be done before attempting to produce an equation.

Lesson 2

✎ Learning objectives
Mental/oral starter:
• Partition to multiply by 2 and 3
Main activity:
• Make and investigate a general statement about shapes

◈ Resources
OHT of tetrominoes and pentominoes (see Main activity for instructions), cut-out L-shaped tromino (see Main activity), pinboards, rubber bands, General Resource Sheet B, square templates of the same size, scissors

ᵃᵇᶜ Vocabulary
Domino, tromino, tetromino, pentomino, square, pattern, rule

MENTAL/ORAL STARTER

Ask children to proffer a range of two-digit numbers which the class has to partition. The children need to multiply these by two and then by three.

MAIN ACTIVITY

Whole class, pairs or small groups

Before the lesson, make an OHT of the full set of tetrominoes and pentominoes shown here:

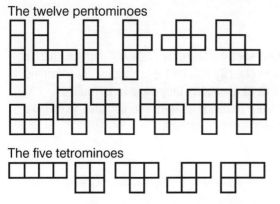

The twelve pentominoes

The five tetrominoes

The intention in this lesson is for the children to work together to find the set of pentominoes (or tetrominoes if more appropriate). Explain that what you want the children to do is to arrange five (or four) squares in as many different ways as they can. The rule is that squares must touch along at least one full side. Draw one domino and two trominoes on the board as shown here to demonstrate how the squares may touch:

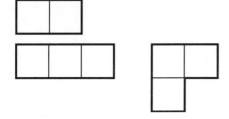

Use the trominoes to talk about duplication. It might be helpful to cut out the L-shape and show how it can look different when rotated or flipped over. The children must have no duplicates in the sets they draw.

Allocate either four or five squares to pairs or small groups and ask them to find all the combinations that they can make. Provide pinboards, rubber bands, squared paper, scissors and templates as appropriate.

■ Support
Explain again about the fact that some combinations may look different but are actually duplicates of others. Cutting out shapes can help with this.

■ Challenge
Invite children to fit tetronimoes or pentominoes together to see what shapes they can make.

PLENARY

Get different pairs to show the shapes that they have found. Use your OHT to check these and show the full set in each case. Cut out examples to convince the children about duplicates as necessary.
How many pentominoes are there?
How many tetronimoes are there?

Key fact or strategy
It is important to organise the approach so that all possible combinations can be found.

Supplementary activities

Mental/oral follow-up

Partitioning to multiply
Extend the multiplication of two-digit numbers through partitioning to the x4 and x6 tables. Be opportunistic in partitioning exercises, for example:
How many in class this morning?
What if there were twice as many?
... six times as many?
... ten times as many?

Homework

Perimeters
Use Resource Sheet 74.

Development

Perimeters
Try developing an equation such as:
Length of side x Number of sides = Perimeter
Then possibly
L x N = P

Pentominoes
Make composite shapes using pentominoes. Then see if the children can work out combinations of pentominoes to make your shape. Make patterns using templates of pentominoes.

ICT ideas

2-D shapes
A "binary tree" program such as *Granada Branch* (Granada Learning) can be used to sort and classify different 2-D shapes. By providing "yes" and "no" answers to questions they have to formulate themselves, children learn to divide shapes into subsets, which are gradually built into binary trees on-screen.

Unit 9   Measures and time

Term				Summer

Framework links

8–10	15	102–111	Shape and space	Recognise reflective symmetry in regular polygons. Complete symmetrical patterns with two lines of symmetry at right angles. Reflect shapes in mirror parallel to one side. Recognise where shape will be after translation.
		76–81	Reasoning about shapes	Make and investigate a general statement about shapes.
		86–101	Measures including problems	Use timetables. Know and use relationship between units of time. Use, read and write standard metric units of capacity, including abbreviations and pint, gallon. Know and use relationships between them. Convert larger to smaller units of capacity, including gallons to pints. Suggest suitable units and equipment to estimate or measure capacity. Read measurements from scales.
				Use all four operations to solve measurement word problems, including time. Choose appropriate operations/calculation methods. Explain working.

Setting the scene

In this unit, the children will be using their now prodigious skills related to time in reading and interpreting timetables and making judgements about timing, how long things take and the appropriate units of time to use in making estimates and calculations. They are also working on standard metric and imperial units for measuring capacity, doing measuring, reading scales and making estimates.

Starting points

In Units 3 and 6 in this school year, the children have already practised reading a 24-hour digital clock and worked on standard measures of length and mass including converting larger units to smaller ones. They have also had opportunities to read scales on rules and balances.

Checking progress

- All children should be able to get information from a timetable. They should know how to measure capacity accurately, demonstrate that they can convert litres to millilitres and know the imperial units, the pint and gallon.
- Children requiring additional support will benefit from extra practice in creating and interpreting timetables. They will also need more work on confirming the relationship between litres and millilitres and on using pints and gallons.
- Some children will have progressed further and be adept at creating, interpreting and setting up challenges related to timetables. They will be confident in using metric and imperial units of capacity and converting one unit to another.

Lesson 1

Learning objectives
Mental/oral starter:
• Recall multiplication facts up to 10 x 10
Main activity:
• Use timetables

Resources
OHT of Resource Sheet 77, photocopies of Resource Sheets 75, 76 and 77

Vocabulary
Hour, minute, time, timetable, 24-hour clock, how long?

MENTAL/ORAL STARTER

In this lesson, work on those multiplications which often prove the trickiest, namely:
• in the ×6 table: 6 × 6, 7 × 6, 8 × 6, 9 × 6
• in the ×7 table: 6 × 7, 7 × 7, 8 × 7, 9 × 7
• in the ×8 table: 6 × 8, 7 × 8, 8 × 8, 9 × 8
• in the ×9 table: 6 × 9, 7 × 9, 8 × 9, 9 × 9.

Write each of them on the board, working out the products. Then rub them off the board and give the children a product, so that they can supply the matching multiplication. Then in quick-fire fashion, ask individual children:
What are six sevens?
... seven eights?
... nine nines?
and so on.

MAIN ACTIVITY

Whole class, individuals, pairs

Ask the children about the purpose of timetables. Display the OHT of Resource Sheet 77 and cover it so that only the list of stations and the first column (06:50 from Edinburgh) is revealed. Talk about the departure times from each station, and, with the children's help, work out how long each part of the journey takes. If the children require more revision about how to interpret a timetable, reveal the next column of times and do some calculating using these.

Tell the children that they should first see how they get along on their own with the hairdressing appointment timetable set out on Resource Sheet 75, before tackling the work on the train timetable with a partner. Give out Resource Sheets 75 and 76. Leave Resource Sheet 77 available for children to take when they are ready.

■ Support
With these children, look down the timeline for each of the stylists in the salon. Then look across the columns to find out what everyone is doing at a range of points throughout the day. Then ask them to tackle the work on Resource Sheet 76, working with a partner if they benefit from talking about how to reach an answer.

■ Challenge
Those children who complete the work related to both the hairdressing salon and the rail timetable can choose one or other of these and create some more challenges for their partner to work through.

PLENARY

Show the children the OHT of Resource Sheet 77 again and work through the answers to the questions there. This gives the opportunity for children who may not have completed the work to think about how to do it.

Key fact or strategy
In interpreting timetables, we need to have knowledge of the 24-hour clock and of the fact that there are 60 minutes in an hour.

Lesson 2

Learning objectives
Mental/oral starter:
- Derive division facts corresponding to tables up to 10 x 10

Main activity:
- Know and use the relationships between units of time

Resources
Resource Sheet 78 photocopied on thin card and cut out, photocopies of Resource Sheets 79 and 80

Vocabulary
Time, unit, second, minute, hour, day, week, year, decade, century

MENTAL/ORAL STARTER

Shuffle and place the product cards made from Resource Sheet 78 in a pile face down on the front desk. Shuffle and place the number cards in a similar pile. Turn up one card from each pile and question the children as follows:
Here's a product: 60, and a number: 10.
Can we make a division using 60 and 10?
60 divided by 10 is 6.
Write on the board:
60 ÷ 10 = 6

Then turn up the next card from each pile. Abandon cards with which it is not possible to make a whole number division. When all the cards have been used, shuffle both piles and use them again.

MAIN ACTIVITY

Whole class, individuals, pairs

Introduce the lesson by writing a chart to show how units of time are related to one another. The chart should look like this:

60 seconds	=	1 minute
60 minutes	=	1 hour
24 hours	=	1 day
7 days	=	1 week
52 weeks	=	1 year
12 months	=	1 year
10 years	=	1 decade
100 years	=	1 century

When the chart is complete, choose a unit at random and invite the children to say what they would measure using this. For example, ask:
What would you measure in seconds? (Winking, blinking, jumping, cracking an egg, clapping hands, signing my name, and so on.)

Then do the same for other units. Reverse the process, giving the children a suggested happening and asking them to say what unit of time measurement they would choose. Here are some examples:
What unit would you use to measure the time it takes to …
… build a house?
… paint a picture?
… play a single?
… wash your face?

Give each child a copy of Resource Sheet 79 and give them time to complete it. They can then move on to working on Resource Sheet 80.

Support

Draw these children's attention to the chart completed at the beginning of the lesson. Give them help in determining what we measure using units of time, and which units are appropriate.

Challenge

Resource Sheet 80 is quite challenging. When completed, the children can talk it through with a partner.

PLENARY

Compare some of the children's answers on Resource Sheet 80, discussing the methods that they used.

Key fact or strategy
We can estimate and measure using standard units of time.

Lesson 3

✎ Learning objectives
Mental/oral starter:
- Find simple percentages

Main activity:
- Use, read and write standard metric units of capacity, including abbreviations and pint, gallon
- Know and use relationships between measures of capacity
- Convert larger to smaller units of capacity, including gallons to pints

📖 Resources
Large 100 square, containers, measuring jugs or cylinders marked in millilitres, buckets, access to water, access to a waterproof surface or outside, pint bottle, gallon bucket, photocopies of Resource Sheets 81 and 82

ᵃᵇᶜ Vocabulary
Capacity, measuring jug, measuring cylinder, litre (l), millilitre (ml), pint, gallon

MENTAL/ORAL STARTER

Remind the children that a percentage is a part of a whole if the whole were cut into 100 parts. Show them the 100 square (the whole) and point out that 50 parts or squares is 50%, 20 squares is 20%, and so on.

To allow the children practice in working out simple percentages, they can be given some capacity puzzles. Check that they can work out what percentage of one litre the following volumes are:
500 ml
250 ml
750 ml
100 ml
50 ml

Then ask them for similar percentages of a range of numbers including, for example, 500, 200 and 10 000.

MAIN ACTIVITY

Whole class, pairs or small groups, individuals

Before the lesson, set out equipment for each work group. Each group needs access to five containers, such as plastic beakers, boxes, egg cups and bowls of differing sizes. Each group also needs measuring jugs or cylinders and a bucket of water. The work should be done on a waterproof surface or outside.

First, demonstrate to the children how to measure the capacity of a container by filling it right to the top before decanting the contents very carefully into a measuring cylinder or jug.

Then introduce them to the other two important exercises in the lesson, namely conversion from litres to millilitres and from gallons to pints. Do this by checking that they already know that there are 1 000 millilitres in one litre. Then hold up the pint bottle and the gallon bucket and ask the children to estimate how many pints there are in a gallon. Tell them that there are eight. Write on the board:
1 000 ml = 1 l
8 pints = 1 gallon

Also write:
1 pint is about 570 ml
1 litre is about 1¾ pints

Allow the children, in their groups, to measure the capacity of the five containers given to them. Impress on the children that they should all have a go at measuring the capacity of each container. The outcomes can be recorded on Resource Sheet 81. When the measuring is done, the children can work alone on the conversions which are also on Resource Sheet 81.

Resource Sheet 82 offers the children an opportunity to demonstrate their knowledge of the relationships between units.

■ Support
Allow these children extra practice in measuring and recording capacities. Help them with conversion and the relationships between units by offering clues and strategic questions.

■ Challenge

Use some peer tutoring by asking children who are confident with the ideas to give extra support to those who are finding the completion of Resource Sheet 82 difficult.

Key fact or strategy

There are 1 000 ml in 1 litre, 8 pints in 1 gallon and about 570 ml in 1 pint.

PLENARY

Work through Resource Sheet 82 with the children's help, checking on their misconceptions.

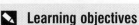

Lesson 4

■ **Learning objectives**

Mental/oral starter:
- Convert litres to millilitres

Main activity:
- Suggest suitable units and equipment to estimate and measure capacity
- Read measurements from scales
- Round measures of capacity or volume to the nearest litre

■ **Resources**

Capacity workshop (see Main activity), whiteboard or large sheet of paper

■ **Vocabulary**

Capacity, measuring jug, measuring cylinder, litre (l), millilitre (ml), pint, gallon

MENTAL/ORAL STARTER

Write up some figures in litres on the board. Ask the children to convert each in turn to millilitres. Here are some "litre strings" for discussion:

1 litre, 2 litres, 3 litres
… continue up to 10 litres.
10 litres, 20 litres … continue up to 100 litres.
12 litres, 120 litres, 1 200 litres …
1 litre, 0.1 litre, 0.01 litre …

Add to this list with "strings" that demonstrate place value and the relationship between litres and millilitres.

MAIN ACTIVITY

Whole class, small groups

Before the lesson, set up a capacity workshop with four or five work spots that the children can visit around the room. In each of these, there need to be about four challenges, with instructions written on card. The equipment required will depend on the challenges set. Remember to mask any volumes.

Here are suggestions for the four work spots around the room:

- **Work spot 1**

Challenge: Estimate how many ml.
Provide a half full bottle of oil, a cup of washing-up liquid, some coloured water in beaker and some wash liquid in a saucer.

- **Work spot 2**

Challenge: How much is here? Read the scales.
Provide pictures of measuring cylinders 1, 2, 3 and 4 with different volumes marked on the scales.

- **Work spot 3**

Challenge: Estimate how many ml, l, pints or gallons.
Provide a bucket three quarters full of water, a water tray with 3 gallons (15 litres in it) and three 2-litre bottles of water or squash.

- **Work spot 4**

Challenge: Read these scales, and record how much is there.
Provide two medicine cups, one with 5 ml and the other with 20 ml of coloured water, and two measuring jugs, one with 600 ml of cold tea and the other with 250 ml of squash.

As an introduction, ask the children to make some suggestions about what they might measure in litres and then in millilitres. Here are some suggestions, which might begin the lists:

• in litres: milk, bath water, wash liquid for clothes, petrol
• in millilitres: medicine, fizzy drink, washing-up liquid, wine.

Then ask:
What unit would you use to measure a spoonful?
… a cupful?
… a glassful?
… a bowlful?
… a bathful?
… a bucketful?
… a puddle?
… a waterbuttful?

Allow the children to visit each of the four or five work spots in their groups. They should look at each of the challenges and write their answers down in their exercise books.

■ Support
Visit the groups and check that each child is able to make their contribution to the discussion and to make their own record of their estimates and readings.

■ Challenge
These children can begin the rounding exercise, which will be discussed in the plenary session.

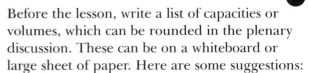

PLENARY

Before the lesson, write a list of capacities or volumes, which can be rounded in the plenary discussion. These can be on a whiteboard or large sheet of paper. Here are some suggestions:

900 ml
550 ml
2 800 ml
6 090 ml
4$\frac{3}{4}$ litres
10$\frac{9}{10}$ litres
7.7 litres

Ask the children to round each one to the nearest litre.

> **Key fact or strategy**
> We measure capacity in litres or millilitres, pints or gallons, according to which is more appropriate.

Supplementary activities

Mental/oral follow-up

Conversion game
Play a conversion game with the children, involving:
£ to p
m to cm
km to m
kg to g
l to ml

This can be done by writing the list above on the board. Then place the class in five groups giving each group a number from one to five. Group one becomes £ to pence, and so on. Then call out a number and get each group to make the appropriate conversion in turn. If the number is, for example, 35, the groups should act as follows:
Group

1	£ to p	£35	=	3500p
2	m to cm	35 m	=	3500 cm
3	km to m	35 km	=	35000 m
4	kg to g	35 kg	=	35000 g
5	l to ml	35 l	=	35000 ml

Call out other numbers in turn, giving them decimals such as 1.5 towards the ends of the sessions.

Homework

Timetables
There is some more work using the Aberdeen to Oxenholme rail timetable on Resource Sheet 83, which the children can take home to try.

Estimating times
Resource Sheet 84 gives the children some opportunities to estimate times.

Development

Timetables
Offer the children some more experience of timetables. Here are some suggestions:
• Find timetables for local buses or trains, and devise challenges using these.
• Invite the children to pretend they are planning an athletics events day. They should decide on a number of events, plan their timings (which will overlap but not on the same parts of the arena). The arena can be drawn, the timetable made out and a series of challenges related to the timetable for the day can be written out for classmates to solve.
• Use Resource Sheet 85 to begin a set of puzzles to solve related to tide tables.

Capacity in science
Work on science experiments where capacities need to be estimated and measured. Here are some starter questions:

How much pancake batter do we need to put in a pan to make a perfectly circular pancake?

How much rainfall do we get in one month?

How much cake mixture makes a fairy cake to fill the cake paper?

Capacity scales
List and draw all the instruments which have on them a scale in millilitres or litres. Set alongside the kinds of measuring that they are used for.

ICT ideas

Standard metric units
Maths Explorer: Shape and Space (Granada Learning) includes activities relating to all of the standard metric units covered this year. The "All about" section of this CD-ROM is particularly useful as it allows the user to see and understand the contexts involved in the various measures investigations. The children should work through the activities either in pairs or small groups.

Triangles

Label each triangle **equilateral**, **scalene** or **isosceles**.

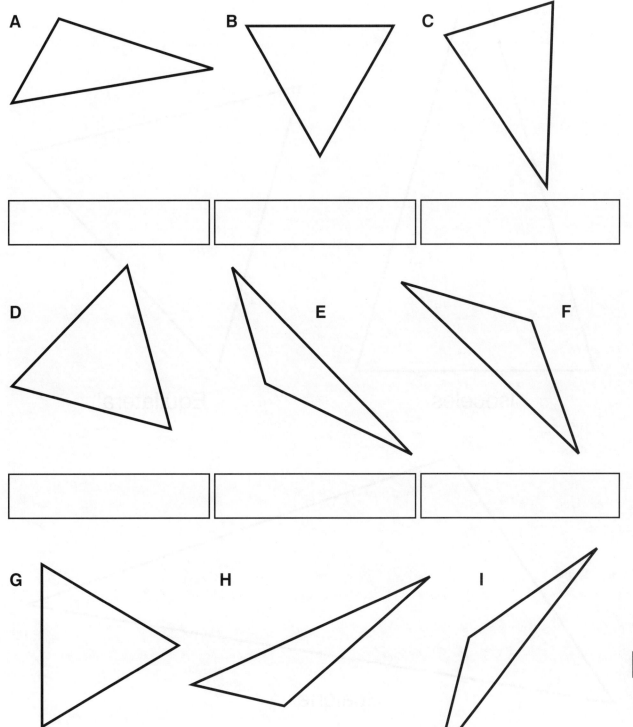

A

B

C

D

E

F

G

H

I

Maths Action Plans, Measures, Shape and Space Year 5/P6 © David Clemson and Wendy Clemson, Nelson Thornes Ltd, 2002

Types of triangles

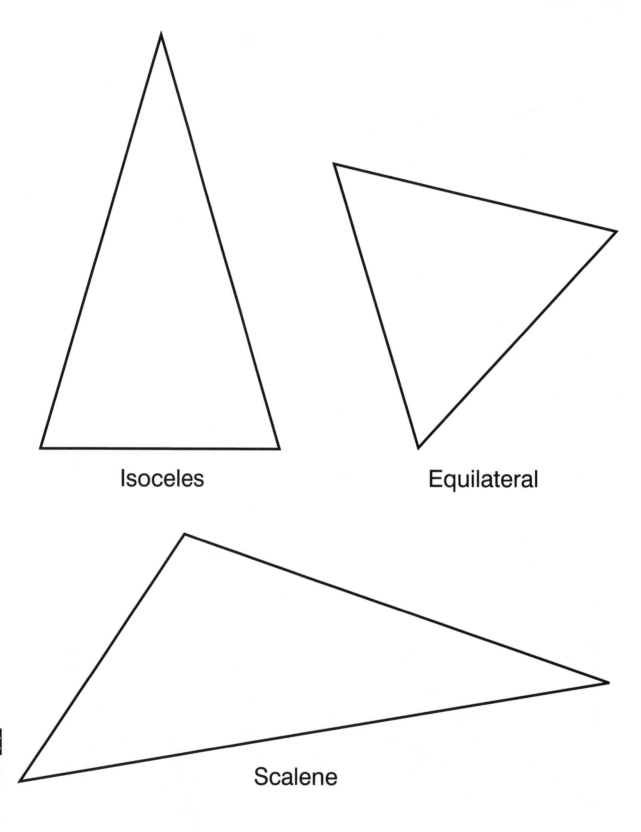

Isoceles

Equilateral

Scalene

Maths Action Plans, Measures, Shape and Space Year 5/P6 © David Clemson and Wendy Clemson, Nelson Thornes Ltd, 2002

Co-ordinates and 2-D shapes

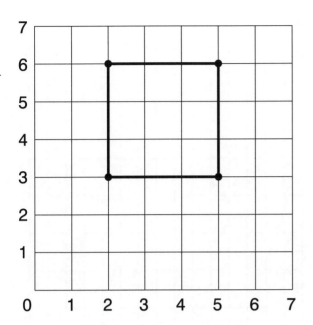

A What are the co-ordinates of this square?

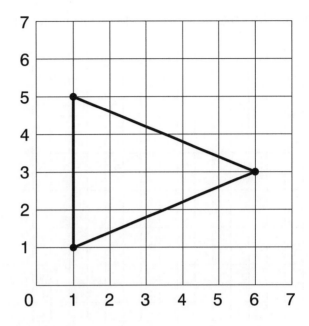

B What are the co-ordinates of this isosceles triangle?

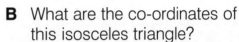

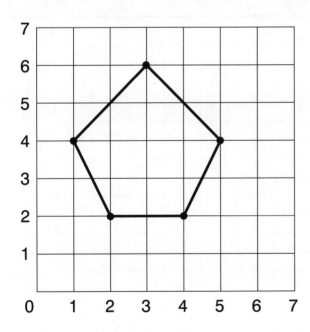

C What are the co-ordinates of this pentagon?

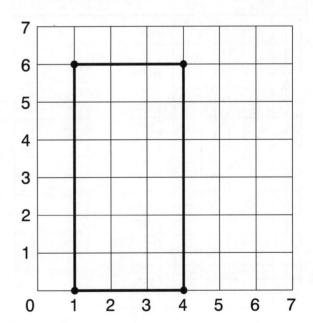

D What are the co-ordinates of this rectangle?

Resource sheet 3

Draw the shapes

Mark the axes on each grid then draw the shape.

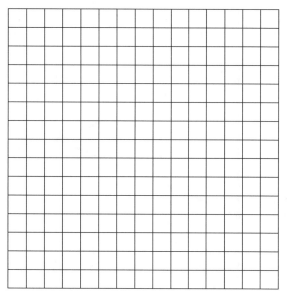 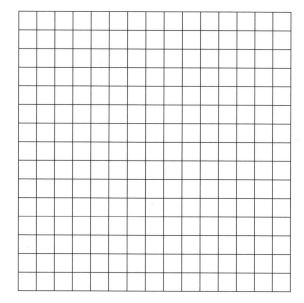

A Co-ordinates: (3, 2) (13, 2) (5, 7)

B Co-ordinates: (2, 5) (11, 5) (4, 10)
(9, 10)

Shape name:

Shape name:

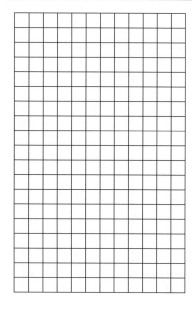 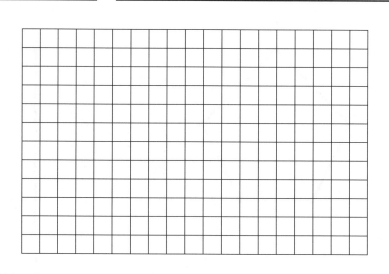

C Co-ordinates: (2, 9) (5, 6) (8, 9)
(2, 12) (5, 15) (8, 12)

D Co-ordinates: (2, 2) (13, 2) (2, 9)
(13, 9) (19, 6)

Shape name:

Shape name:

Missing co-ordinates

Label the axes and put in the missing co-ordinates to make the shapes.

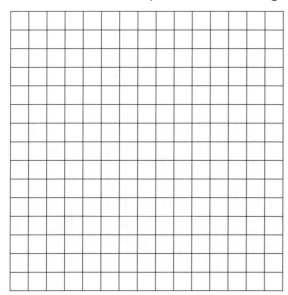

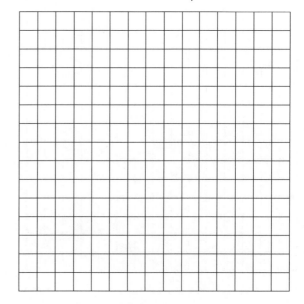

A Three of the co-ordinates for this square are (2, 3) (9, 3) (2, 10). What is the missing one?

B Three of the co-ordinates for this trapezium are (5, 5) (4, 10) (11, 10). What is the missing one?

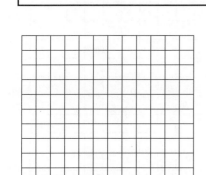

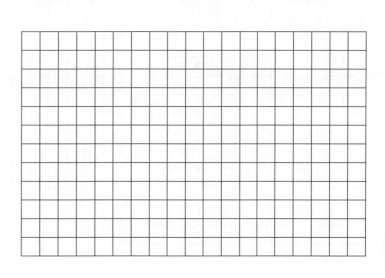

C Three of the co-ordinates for this rectangle are (5, 1) (5, 17) (2, 17). What is the missing one?

D Three of the co-ordinates for this parallelogram are (3, 0) (6, 9) (19, 9). What is the missing one?

Resource sheet 5

Grids

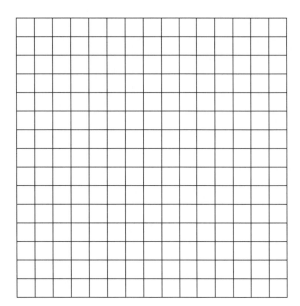

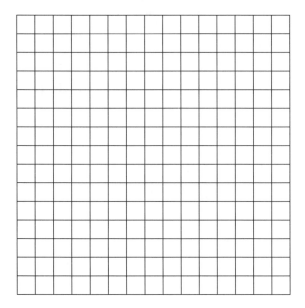

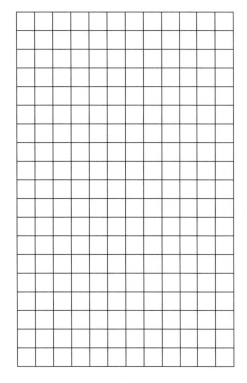

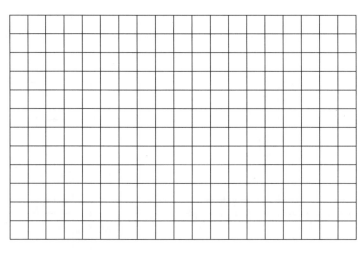

Rectangles

The corners of all rectangles are always

The opposite sides of all rectangles are

The diagonals of rectangles cross and

Find the rectangles

Which of these are rectangles? Colour the rectangles.

Maths Action Plans, Measures, Shape and Space Year 5/P6 © David Clemson and Wendy Clemson, Nelson Thornes Ltd, 2002

Resource sheet 8

Solve these

A With twelve squares you can make three different rectangles.

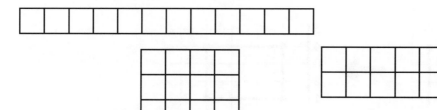

Find how many squares you need to make exactly five rectangles.

B How many rectangles are there here?

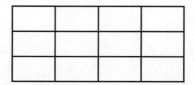

C A pentomino is a shape made from five identical squares touching edge to edge. Here are two:

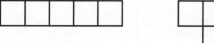 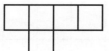

Now divide this shape into two pentominoes.
Do it in four different ways, using a different colour for each way.

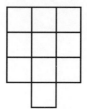

Changing grids (1)

Here is a square drawn on a grid. Look what happens if we "stretch" the x–axis.

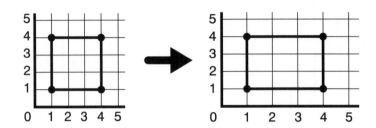

Now draw what happens with these. Explain what has happened in each case.

A

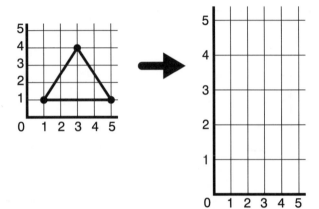

Explain:

B

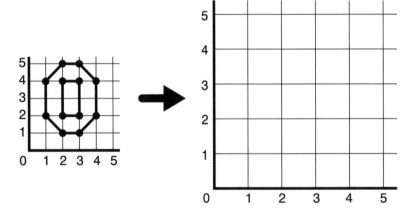

Explain:

C Now make up one of your own.

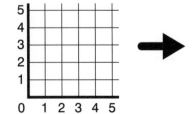

Explain:

Maths Action Plans, Measures, Shape and Space Year 5/P6 © David Clemson and Wendy Clemson, Nelson Thornes Ltd, 2002

Changing grids (2)

Transform this letter X.

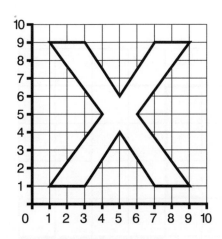
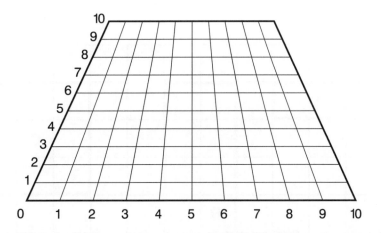

Now make up some transformations of your own.
First draw the shapes on squared paper, then transform them on these grids.

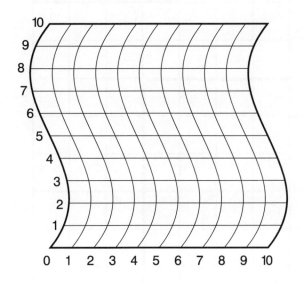
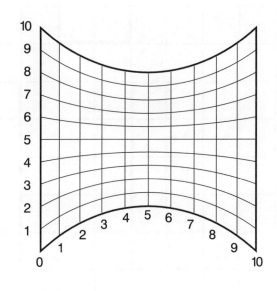

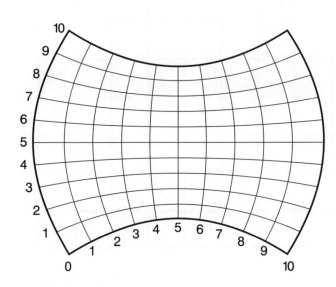
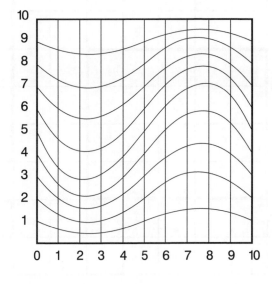

Maths Action Plans, Measures, Shape and Space Year 5/P6 © David Clemson and Wendy Clemson, Nelson Thornes Ltd, 2002

Areas of rectangles (1)

This grid is made out of centimetre squares.
Work out the area of the rectangles.

Maths Action Plans, Measures, Shape and Space Year 5/P6 © David Clemson and Wendy Clemson, Nelson Thornes Ltd, 2002

74

Areas of rectangles (2)

What are the areas of the rectangles? Measure and work out each one using the rule you have written down.

A

B

C

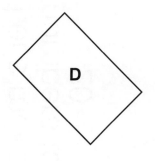

D

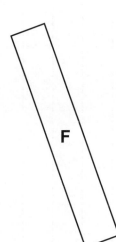

E

F

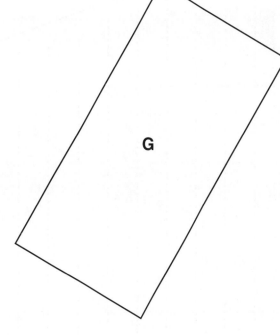

G

Maths Action Plans, Measures, Shape and Space Year 5/P6 © David Clemson and Wendy Clemson, Nelson Thornes Ltd, 2002

Addition pairs booklet (1)

RESOURCE SHEET **14**

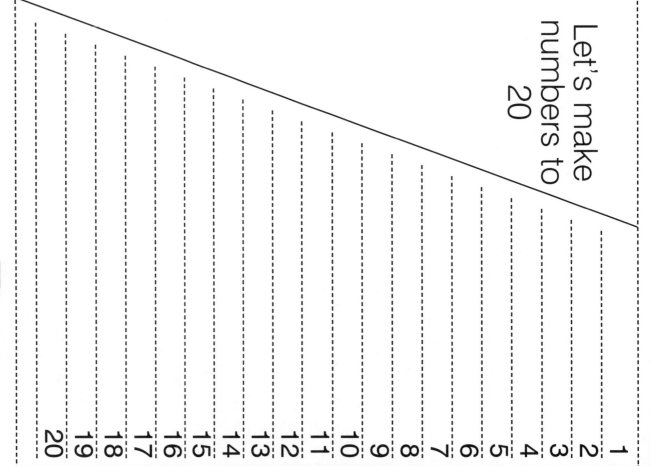

Let's make numbers to 20

1
2
3
4
5
6
7
8
9
10
11
12
13
14
15
16
17
18
19
20

Addition pairs booklet (2)

Glue here

Fold here

0 + 1

0 + 2, 1 + 1

0 + 3, 1 + 2

0 + 4, 1 + 3, 2 + 2

0 + 5, 1 + 4, 2 + 3

0 + 6, 1 + 5, 2 + 4, 3 + 3

0 + 7, 1 + 6, 2 + 5, 3 + 4

0 + 8, 1 + 7, 2 + 6, 3 + 5, 4 + 4

0 + 9, 1 + 8, 2 + 7, 3 + 6, 4 + 5

0 + 10, 1 + 9, 2 + 8, 3 + 7, 4 + 6, 5 + 5

0 + 11, 1 + 10, 2 + 9, 3 + 8, 4 + 7, 5 + 6

0 + 12, 1 + 11, 2 + 10, 3 + 9, 4 + 8, 5 + 7, 6 + 6

0 + 13, 1 + 12, 2 + 11, 3 + 10, 4 + 9, 5 + 8, 6 + 7

0 + 14, 1 + 13, 2 + 12, 3 + 11, 4 + 10, 5 + 9, 6 + 8, 7 + 7

0 + 15, 1 + 14, 2 + 13, 3 + 12, 4 + 11, 5 + 10, 6 + 9, 7 + 8

0 + 16, 1 + 15, 2 + 14, 3 + 13, 4 + 12, 5 + 11, 6 + 10, 7 + 9, 8 + 8

0 + 17, 1 + 16, 2 + 15, 3 + 14, 4 + 13, 5 + 12, 6 + 11, 7 + 10, 8 + 9

0 + 18, 1 + 17, 2 + 16, 3 + 15, 4 + 14, 5 + 13, 6 + 12, 7 + 11, 8 + 10, 9 + 9

0 + 19, 1 + 18, 2 + 17, 3 + 16, 4 + 15, 5 + 14, 6 + 13, 7 + 12, 8 + 11, 9 + 10

0 + 20, 1 + 19, 2 + 18, 3 + 17, 4 + 16, 5 + 15, 6 + 14, 7 + 13, 8 + 12, 9 + 11, 10 + 10

Resource sheet 15

Perimeters of rectangles (1)

Measure and write in the perimeter of each of these rectangles.

A _____

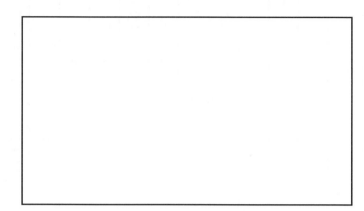

B _____

C _____

D _____

E _____

F _____

G _____

Perimeters of rectangles (2)

A Use what you know about how to work out the perimeter of a rectangle to calculate the perimeters of rectangles with these dimensions:

Length	Breadth	Perimeter
6 cm	4 cm	
17 m	2 m	
14 mm	3 mm	

B Work out the length of the mystery side of these rectangles.

	Perimeter	Longer side	Shorter side
Rectangle 1	36 cm	10 cm	
Rectangle 2	36 cm		6 cm
Rectangle 3	32 m	14 m	
Rectangle 4	1 km		0.2 km

C If a rectangle has a pair of sides of length **L** and a pair of sides of length **S**, can you write a sentence describing how to work out the perimeter **P** of the rectangle?

Resource sheet 17

Maths Action Plans, Measures, Shape and Space Year 5/P6 © David Clemson and Wendy Clemson, Nelson Thornes Ltd, 2002

Perimeters of polygons

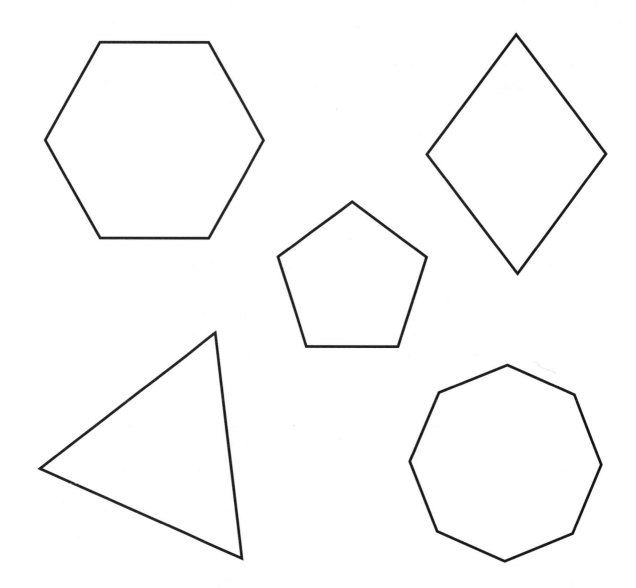

These are all regular polygons.
- a polygon is a 2-D shape with straight sides
- a regular polygon has all sides of the same length.

Can you write down an expression which tells us how to calculate the perimeter of any regular polygon?

Maths Action Plans, Measures, Shape and Space Year 5/P6 © David Clemson and Wendy Clemson, Nelson Thornes Ltd, 2002

Measuring carefully

A Measure these lines carefully in millimetres and write in the measurements.

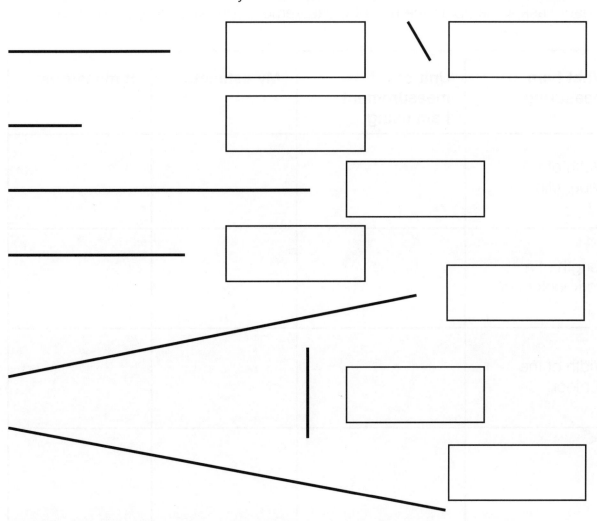

B Draw and label lines of these lengths:

17 mm, 36 mm, 150 mm, 10.2 cm

Maths Action Plans, Measures, Shape and Space Year 5/P6 © David Clemson and Wendy Clemson, Nelson Thornes Ltd, 2002

Units of measurement

Use the list of items your teacher gives you to do some measuring.
For each task, think about the unit of measurement you will use and write it in.

What I am measuring	Unit of measurement I am using	My estimate	It measures
Width of a paper clip			
Length of a workbook page			
Width of the corridor			

Maths Action Plans, Measures, Shape and Space Year 5/P6 © David Clemson and Wendy Clemson, Nelson Thornes Ltd, 2002

Metric measures

A Which is longer? Circle the answer.

4 metres	*or*	40 centimetres
10 km	*or*	10 m
100 mm	*or*	9 m

Which is longest? Circle the answer.

300 cm	330 m	3 300 mm
10.02 km	100.2 m	1 000 m
107 mm	1.07 cm	0.0107 km

B Change these into metres (m).

89 km ☐

1.5 km ☐

0.25 km ☐

Change these into centimetres (cm).

1.75 m ☐   0.25 m ☐

1 m ☐   10 m ☐

5.5 m ☐

Change these into millimetres (mm).

10 cm ☐   0.3 cm ☐

80 cm ☐   5.5 cm ☐

Maths Action Plans, Measures, Shape and Space Year 5/P6 © David Clemson and Wendy Clemson, Nelson Thornes Ltd, 2002

Resource sheet 21

Imperial and metric measures

Some family facts

Metric			Imperial		
10 millimetres (mm)	=	1 cm	12 inches (in)	=	1 foot
100 centimetres (cm)	=	1 m	3 feet (ft)	=	1 yard
1000 metres (m)	=	1 km	1760 yards (yd)	=	1 mile

Use this information to help you answer the questions:

1 inch (in) is about 25 mm.
1 metre (m) is about 39 inches.

A Which is longer: a yard or a metre?

B How many centimetres in a foot?

C How many kilometres in a mile?

D What is your height in cm?

Convert this to an approximate imperial measure.

Maths Action Plans, Measures, Shape and Space Year 5/P6 © David Clemson and Wendy Clemson, Nelson Thornes Ltd, 2002

Clock face

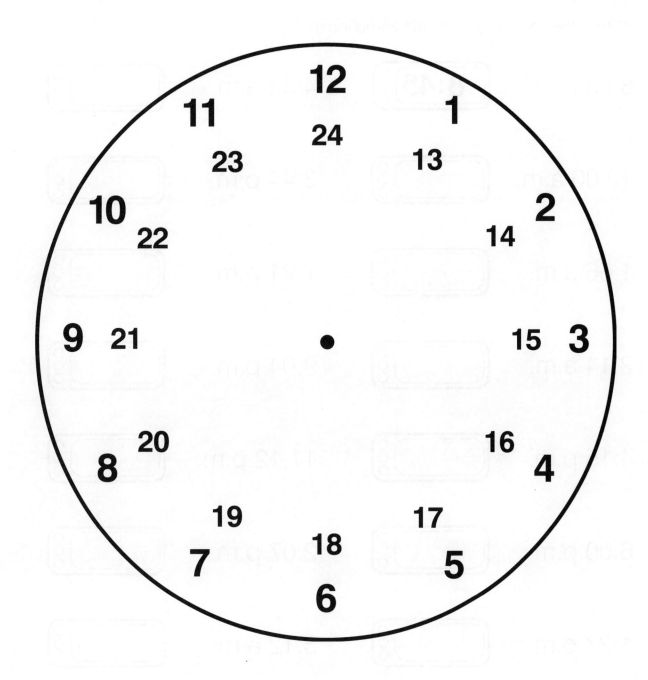

Digital clock

Write in the correct times on the 24-hour digital clocks.

8:45 a.m.    4:32 a.m.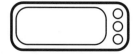

10:00 a.m. 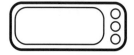   3:44 p.m.

1:56 a.m. 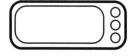   7:21 p.m.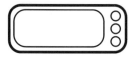

2:14 a.m. 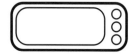   9:04 p.m.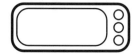

4:15 p.m. 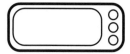   11:12 p.m.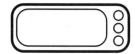

6:00 p.m. 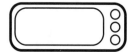   2:07 p.m.

1:27 p.m. 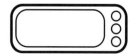   3:12 a.m.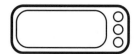

 10:19 p.m.    5:49 p.m.

5:57 p.m. 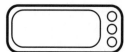   8:51 p.m.

Time cards

Cut out each card.

2:14	**2:14** a.m.	**14:14**	**2:14** p.m.
15:36	**3:36** p.m.	**3:36**	**3:36** a.m.
5:42	**5:42** a.m.	**17:42**	**5:42** p.m.
18:23	**6:23** p.m.	**6:23**	**6:23** a.m.
7:19	**7:19** a.m.	**19:19**	**7:19** p.m.
20:08	**8:08** p.m.	**8:08**	**8:08** a.m.
9:49	**9:49** a.m.	**21:49**	**9:49** p.m.
22:02	**10:02** p.m.	**10:02**	**10:02** a.m.
11:11	**11:11** a.m.	**23:11**	**11:11** p.m.

Maths Action Plans, Measures, Shape and Space Year 5/P6 © David Clemson and Wendy Clemson, Nelson Thornes Ltd, 2002

Resource sheet 25

Measuring game

Invent a game where the players have to decide which measuring tool (and unit) is best for measuring the length, width or height of some things.

You could make it a board game or a card game.

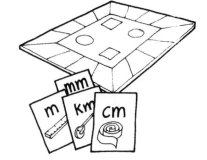

You need to draw all the possible tools, for example:

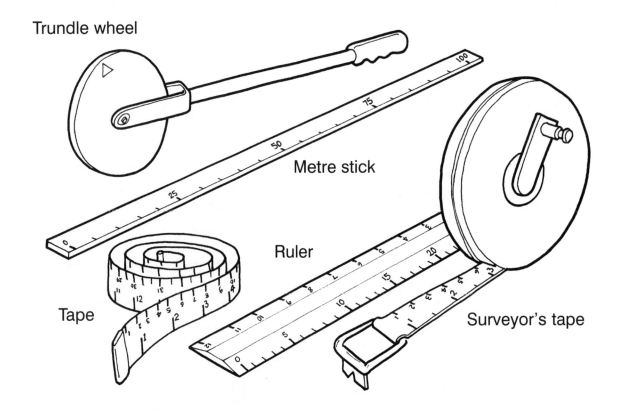

Trundle wheel

Metre stick

Ruler

Tape

Surveyor's tape

You may need to draw some measuring dilemmas:

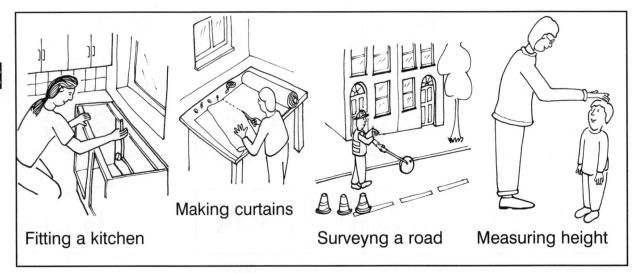

Fitting a kitchen

Making curtains

Surveyng a road

Measuring height

Start numbers

Photocopy on card and cut out.

−10	−5	−0.5	0
2	5	10	20
50	100	300	6
12	36	16	27
49	56	63	72
8	88	42	94
17	40	64	18
45	5000	25	1000
0.5	2.5	7.5	0.1

Resource sheet 27

Counting steps

Photocopy on card and cut out.

0.1	0.2	0.3	0.4
0.5	0.6	0.7	0.8
0.9	1.0	1.25	1.5
2	5	10	25
75	100	200	1000
3	4	6	7
8	9	90	50
500	150	15	40
0.25	0.75	10.5	20

Looking at shapes

Work out what goes in each section of the table for six different shapes.

Name of shape	Number of faces (F), edges(E) and vertices (V)	Shapes of faces	Is any face right-angled?	How many edges meet at each vertex?
	F E V			

2-D pictures of 3-D shapes

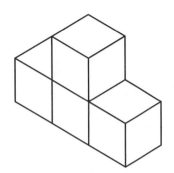

A How many cubes?

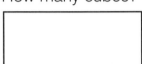

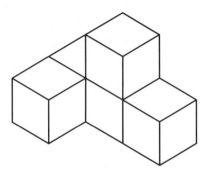

B How many cubes?

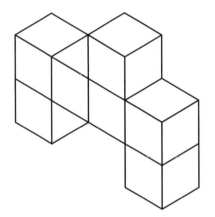

C How many cubes?

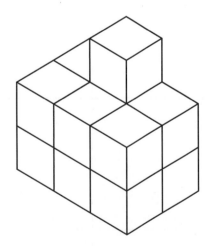

D How many cubes?

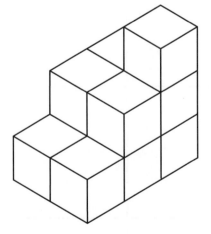

E How many cubes?

Maths Action Plans, Measures, Shape and Space Year 5/P6 © David Clemson and Wendy Clemson, Nelson Thornes Ltd, 2002

Make the cuboid

How many more cubes are needed to make each of these shapes into a **cuboid**?

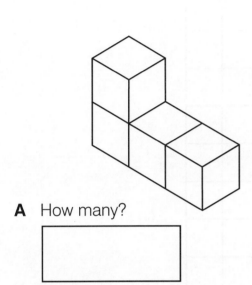

A How many?

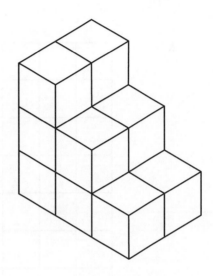

B How many?

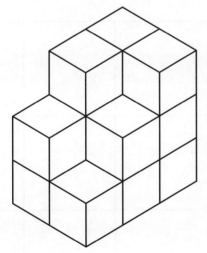

C How many?

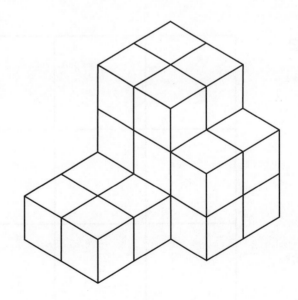

D How many?

Make an open cube

Use the squared paper **B** at the bottom of the page, to draw, cut out and make an open cube. Then use the grid **A** to draw the net of the cube you have made. Colour your net.

A

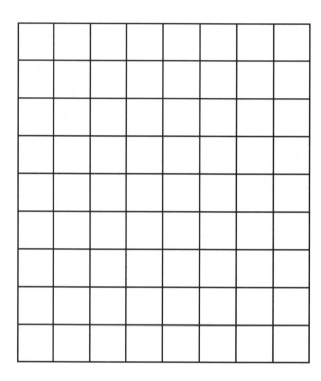

B

Maths Action Plans, Measures, Shape and Space Year 5/P6 © David Clemson and Wendy Clemson, Nelson Thornes Ltd, 2002

Nets of open cubes

Try drawing some nets for open cubes. One is drawn for you.

Maths Action Plans, Measures, Shape and Space Year 5/P6 © David Clemson and Wendy Clemson, Nelson Thornes Ltd, 2002

95

Perpendicular and parallel lines

A With your group, find three examples of perpendicular and three examples of parallel lines in your classroom. Write down where they are.

Perpendicular	Parallel

B With your group, find three examples of perpendicular and three examples of parallel lines around school.

Perpendicular	Parallel

Maths Action Plans, Measures, Shape and Space Year 5/P6 © David Clemson and Wendy Clemson, Nelson Thornes Ltd, 2002

Looking at lines

Look at these drawings of 2-D shapes.
Are there any perpendicular or parallel lines in them?
Write down any ideas you have next to each shape.

Maths Action Plans, Measures, Shape and Space Year 5/P6 © David Clemson and Wendy Clemson, Nelson Thornes Ltd, 2002

97

What's the angle

A Label each angles **acute**, **obtuse** or **right angle**.

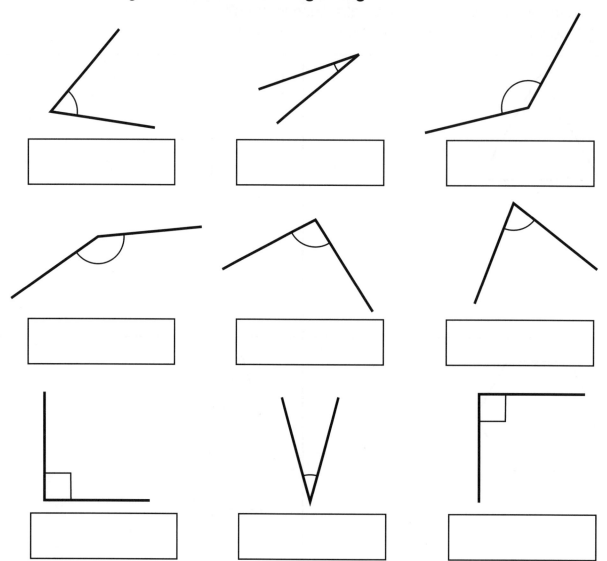

B Write your own definitions:

An acute angle is

A right angle is

An obtuse angle is

Maths Action Plans, Measures, Shape and Space Year 5/P6 © David Clemson and Wendy Clemson, Nelson Thornes Ltd, 2002

Finding angles

A Find two of each of these angles in the classroom.
Write in where you can see them.

Right angle

Acute angle

Obtuse angle

B Look carefully at these shapes. Identify the marked angles by writing in
A (acute), **O** (obtuse) or **R** (right angle) by each of them.

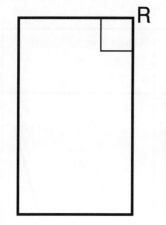
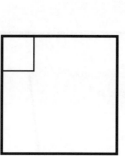
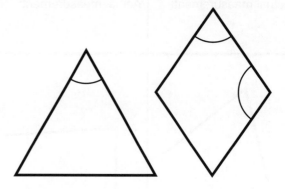

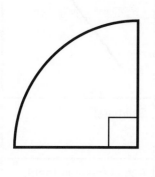
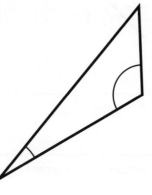
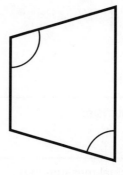
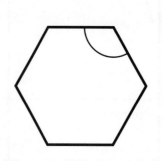

Maths Action Plans, Measures, Shape and Space Year 5/P6 © David Clemson and Wendy Clemson, Nelson Thornes Ltd, 2002

Estimate and measure angles

Estimate the size of each of the angles below. Write in your estimate.
Then measure the angles to the nearest 5° and write in their actual measurements.

Estimate:	Estimate:	Estimate:	Estimate:
Actual measurement:	Actual measurement:	Actual measurement:	Actual measurement:
Estimate:	Estimate:	Estimate:	Estimate:
Actual measurement:	Actual measurement:	Actual measurement:	Actual measurement:

Straight angles

Work out the missing angles in these drawings. Write them in in degrees (°).
Use your protractor to check your answer.

A

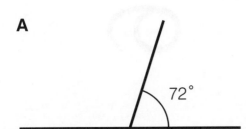

72°

B

40°

C

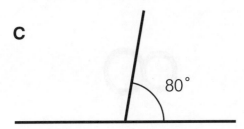

80°

D

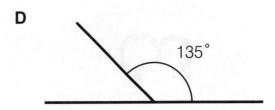

135°

E

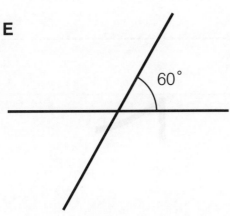

60°

F

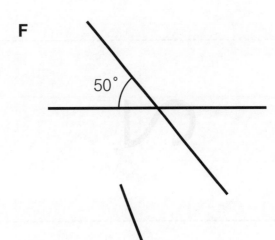

50°

G

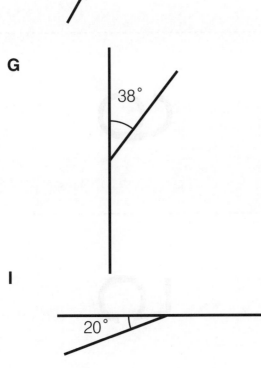

38°

H

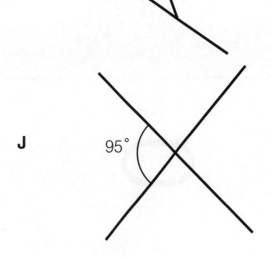

35°

I

20°

J

95°

Maths Action Plans, Measures, Shape and Space Year 5/P6 © David Clemson and Wendy Clemson, Nelson Thornes Ltd, 2002

Digit cards

Photocopy on two colours of card and cut out.

4

9

3

8

2

7

1

6

0

5

Maths Action Plans, Measures, Shape and Space Year 5/P6 © David Clemson and Wendy Clemson, Nelson Thornes Ltd, 2002

Rotations

The shapes below have been turned to make part or complete patterns.
Look at them carefully and answer the questions.

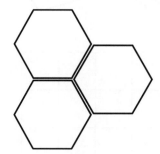

A What is the angle of rotation here?

B What is the angle of rotation here?

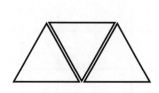

C How many more degrees will the shape need to be turned to complete the pattern?

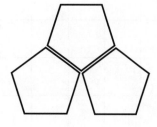

D Why does this shape not fit on an exact number of times when rotated?

E Where will the next shape go if the pattern is continued? Draw it in.

What is the angle of rotation?

F How many times would a square fit in a complete rotation?

Maths Action Plans, Measures, Shape and Space Year 5/P6 © David Clemson and Wendy Clemson, Nelson Thornes Ltd, 2002

Resource sheet 41

Net of a box

Find a small empty box, such as a carton that a toothpaste tube came in or a box that had kitchen herbs in it. Ask an adult whether you may cut the box open. Cut carefully along the edges of sides until the box can be opened out and laid flat. Measure each side and draw a diagram of its net on the grid below.

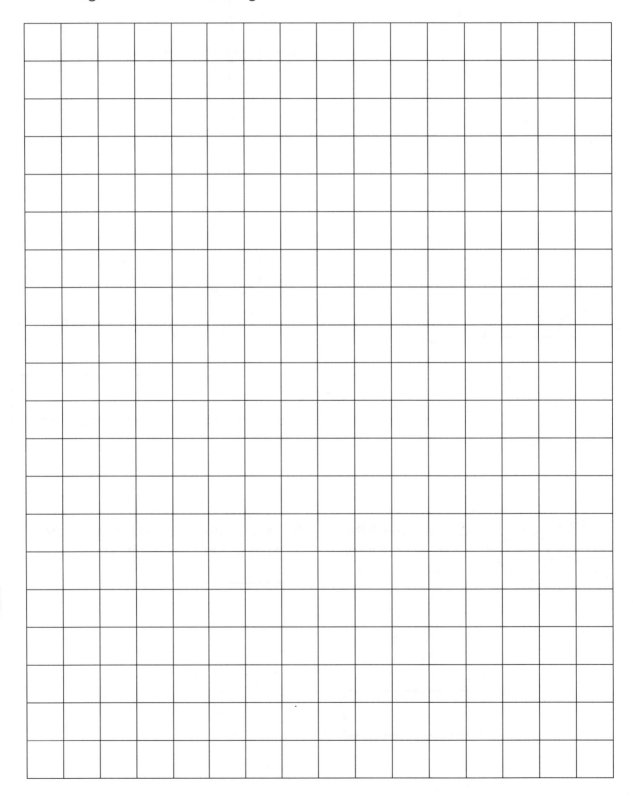

Maths Action Plans, Measures, Shape and Space Year 5/P6 © David Clemson and Wendy Clemson, Nelson Thornes Ltd, 2002

Shapes for rotating

RESOURCE SHEET **43**

Photocopy on card and cut out.

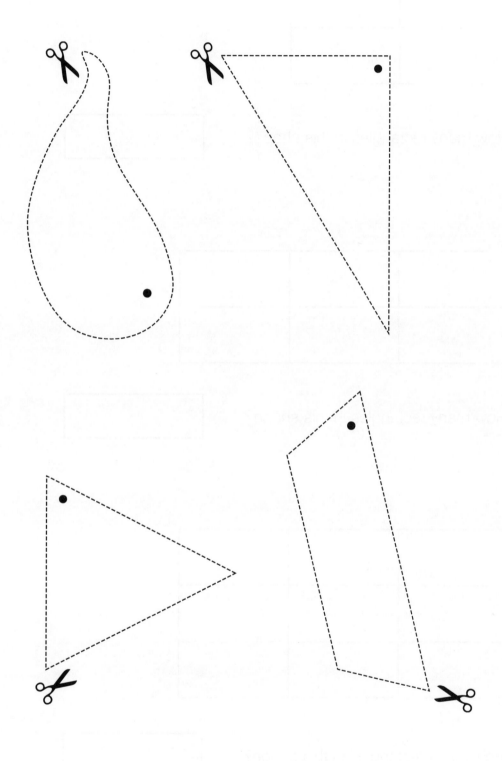

Maths Action Plans, Measures, Shape and Space Year 5/P6 © David Clemson and Wendy Clemson, Nelson Thornes Ltd, 2002

How many rectangles?

A

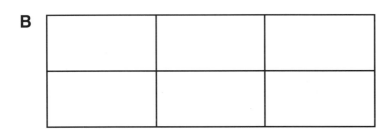

How many rectangles in this shape?

B

How many rectangles in this shape?

C

How many rectangles in this shape?

Maths Action Plans, Measures, Shape and Space Year 5/P6 © David Clemson and Wendy Clemson, Nelson Thornes Ltd, 2002

Angles on a straight line

A Measure the angles and add them up in each case.

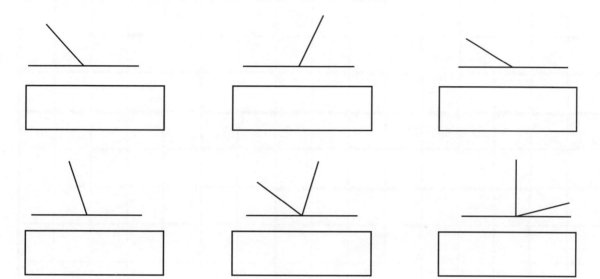

B Draw some examples of your own here and write the angles and their sum.

C Can you make a statement about the angles on a straight line?

Maths Action Plans, Measures, Shape and Space Year 5/P6 © David Clemson and Wendy Clemson, Nelson Thornes Ltd, 2002

Resource sheet 45

Count, then calculate

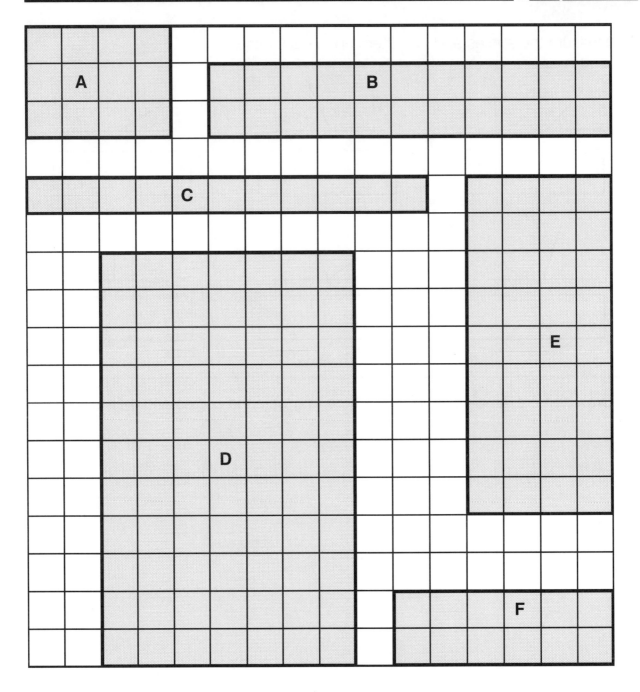

The squares in this grid are centimetre squares (cm²).
Count the squares to determine the area of each of the rectangles.
Then work out the area using the lengths of the sides.

Area of shape	Counting squares	By calculation
A		
B		
C		
D		
E		
F		

Resource sheet 46

Measuring area

Fill in this table for all the estimates and measurements you do.

Object	Estimate length	Estimate breadth or width	Estimate area	Actual length	Actual breadth or width	Actual area	How close were you?

Maths Action Plans, Measures, Shape and Space Year 5/P6 © David Clemson and Wendy Clemson, Nelson Thornes Ltd, 2002

Positive number cards

Photocopy on card and cut out.

5203	672
9111	8902
436	16
722	2012
146	1142
9727	7210

Negative number cards

Photocopy on card and cut out.

–1	–2
–30	–8
–307	–3075
–5	–10
–70	–37
–250	–2000

Area workbook (1)

Draw a shape with an area of 55 cm². One side has been drawn for you.

_____

Page 8

★ If you need help ask for Clue card 6

Area workbook

Name ....

Class ....

My definition of area

....
....
....
....

★ If you need help ask for Clue card 1

Page 1

Maths Action Plans, Measures, Shape and Space Year 5/P6 © David Clemson and Wendy Clemson, Nelson Thornes Ltd, 2002

Area workbook (2)

Which pages of puzzles did you get correct?
Which gave you problems? How did you solve them?

Page 1

Page 2

Page 3

Page 4

Page 5

Page 6

Page 8

Did you know that there are 100 mm² in 1 cm² and 10000 cm² in 1 m².

How many mm² in 1 m²?

★ **Clue card 7**

Page 7

Calculate the areas of these rectangles.

5

4

A

3

B

6

3

C

2

Check out the unit in which they are measured.

A The area is

B The area is

C The area is

★ **If you need help ask for Clue card 2**

Page 2

Resource sheet 51

Maths Action Plans, Measures, Shape and Space Year 5/P6 © David Clemson and Wendy Clemson, Nelson Thornes Ltd, 2002

113

Write an expression to show how we calculate the area of a rectangle, using a = area, l = longer side, s = shorter side.

Draw a rectangle which proves the truth of the expression.

Draw here:

 Clue card 6

Page 6

Calculate the areas of these rectangles. They are measured in centimetres but are not drawn to scale.

B 7 5

A 16 4

C 9 25

Area of **A**

Area of **B**

Area of **C**

 **If you need help ask for Clue card 3**

Page 3

Area workbook (4)

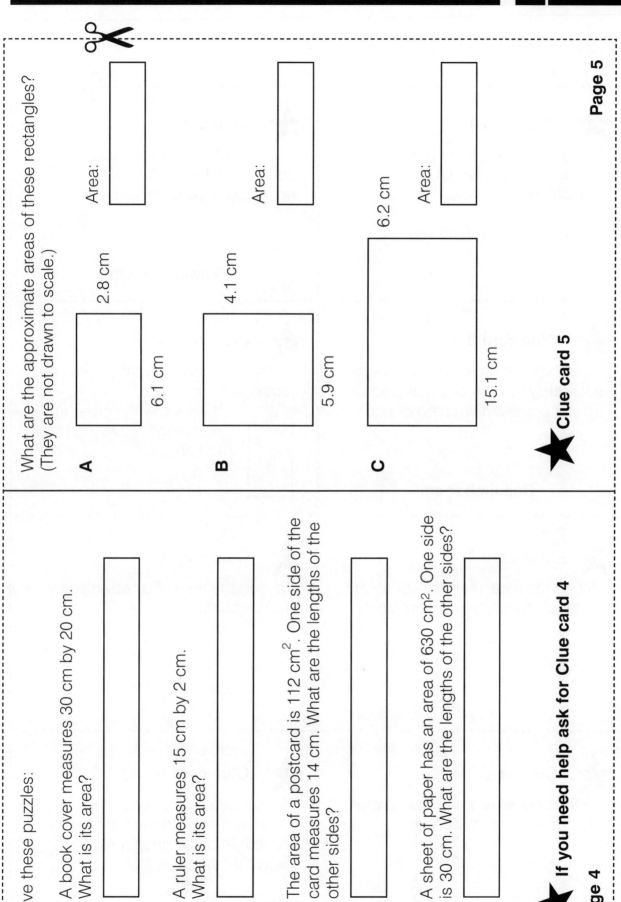

What are the approximate areas of these rectangles?
(They are not drawn to scale.)

A 6.1 cm, 2.8 cm   Area:

B 5.9 cm, 4.1 cm   Area:

C 15.1 cm, 6.2 cm   Area:

★ **Clue card 5**

Page 5

Solve these puzzles:

A A book cover measures 30 cm by 20 cm.
What is its area?

B A ruler measures 15 cm by 2 cm.
What is its area?

C The area of a postcard is 112 cm². One side of the card measures 14 cm. What are the lengths of the other sides?

D A sheet of paper has an area of 630 cm². One side is 30 cm. What are the lengths of the other sides?

★ **If you need help ask for Clue card 4**

Page 4

Clue cards

Photocopy on card and cut out.

 Clue card 1

Has your definition got the words cover, coverage, length and breadth in it?

These words may help you.

 Clue card 2

Use a centimetre rule. Draw squares of 1 cm to fill each rectangle. Count the squares.

Remember cm².

 Clue card 3

If you need to draw the rectangles accurately to work out their areas ask for some cm squared paper.

Remember cm².

 Clue card 4

These puzzles involve the areas of rectangles.

If we know the area (a) and length (l) we can find length (s).

$$\frac{a}{l} = s$$

 Clue card 5

Round the measurements of each rectangle to whole numbers, then multitly.

 Clue card 6

We find the area of a rectangle by multiplication.

 Clue card 7

Write about what went wrong when the answer did not work out.

Clue card 8

Measure the side. Divide this measurement into the area to give the length of the shorter side. Draw the shape.

Kilograms and grams

A What fractions of a kilogram are these?

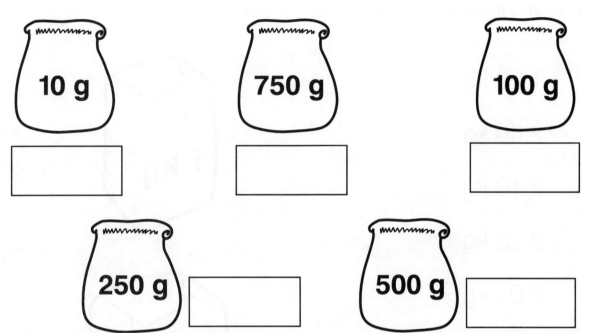

10 g

750 g

100 g

250 g

500 g

B Write these masses in grams:

16.25 kg

7.07 kg

3.5 kg

102.75 kg

52.1 kg

77.01 kg

C Write these masses in kilograms:

7400 g

40 g

3000 g

102 g

8924 g

5360 g

17 g

5 g

Resource sheet 55

Rounding

What are these masses rounded to the nearest kilogram?
Join each to the appropriate mass.

1.25 kg

2.80 kg

2.10 kg

2.25 kg

3.01 kg

1.50 kg

1.75 kg

2.75 kg

3.25 kg

1.10 kg

2.09 kg

3.04 kg

2.97 kg

2.85 kg

Maths Action Plans, Measures, Shape and Space Year 5/P6 © David Clemson and Wendy Clemson, Nelson Thornes Ltd, 2002

Estimate and weigh

Record your weighing tasks here:

Item to be weighed	My estimate. It weighs …	It weighs … in g.	It weighs … in kg.

Maths Action Plans, Measures, Shape and Space Year 5/P6 © David Clemson and Wendy Clemson, Nelson Thornes Ltd, 2002

Weighing instruments

Which of these instruments would you use to do the weighing jobs below?

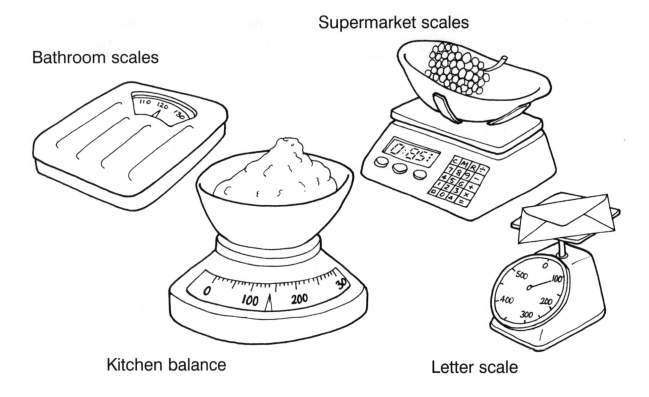

Supermarket scales

Bathroom scales

Kitchen balance

Letter scale

The weight of:

- a bag of potatoes

- sugar for cooking

- grandma

- a bunch of bananas

- a letter

- fat and flour in a cake

- dad

Talk about your answers.

Fractions and percentages

Photocopy on card and cut out. Then separate the cards into a set
of fractions and a set of percentages.

$\frac{1}{10}$	$66\frac{2}{3}\%$	25%	75%
$\frac{1}{5}$	$\frac{3}{10}$	$12\frac{1}{2}\%$	$\frac{7}{10}$
$\frac{9}{10}$	$\frac{2}{5}$	$\frac{1}{2}$	$\frac{4}{5}$
$\frac{2}{3}$	$\frac{1}{4}$	$\frac{3}{5}$	$\frac{1}{3}$
10%	$\frac{1}{8}$	$\frac{3}{4}$	70%
20%	30%	50%	80%
90%	40%	60%	$33\frac{1}{3}\%$

Resource sheet 59

Maths Action Plans, Measures, Shape and Space Year 5/P6 © David Clemson and Wendy Clemson, Nelson Thornes Ltd, 2002

Reflective symmetry (1)

Cut out each shape and fold it or use a ruler to find out whether it shows reflective symmetry.

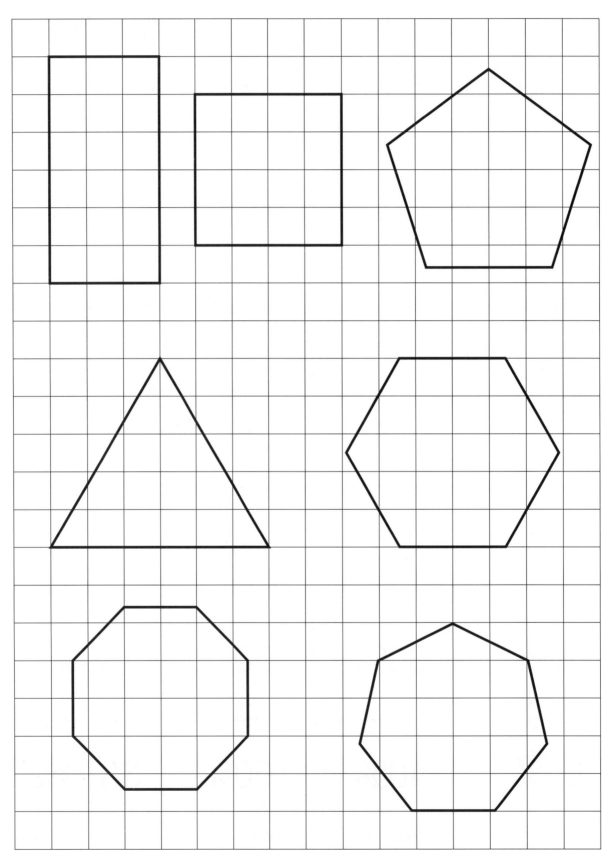

Maths Action Plans, Measures, Shape and Space Year 5/P6 © David Clemson and Wendy Clemson, Nelson Thornes Ltd, 2002

Reflective symmetry (2)

Cut out each shape and fold it or use a ruler to find out whether
it shows reflective symmetry.

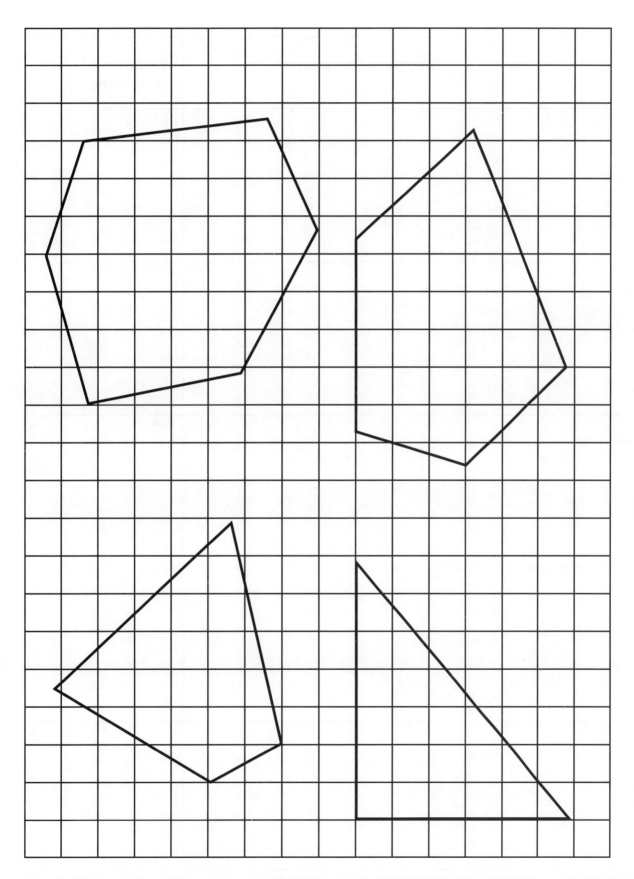

Maths Action Plans, Measures, Shape and Space Year 5/P6 © David Clemson and Wendy Clemson, Nelson Thornes Ltd, 2002

How many lines of symmetry?

Choose five different regular polygons. Write the name of each one.
Draw it accurately and record how many lines of symmetry it has.

Name of shape	Drawing of the shape	Number of lines of symmetry

Reflect the shapes (1)

Draw in the reflections of these shapes.

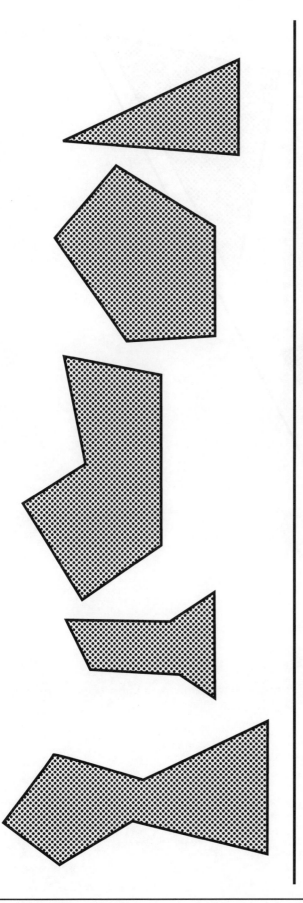

Mirror line

Maths Action Plans, Measures, Shape and Space Year 5/P6 © David Clemson and Wendy Clemson, Nelson Thornes Ltd, 2002

Resource sheet 63

Reflect the shapes (2)

Draw the reflections of the shapes.

Mirror line

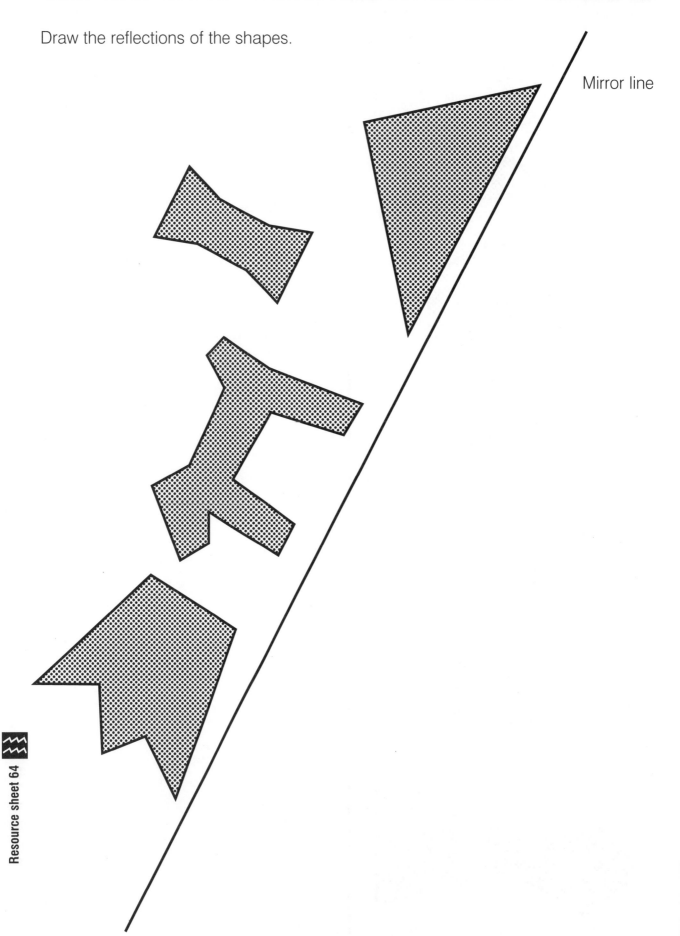

Two-digit cards

Photocopy on card and cut out.

10	11	12	13	14	15	16	17
18	19	20	21	22	23	24	25
26	27	28	29	30	31	32	33
34	35	36	37	38	39	40	41
42	43	44	45	46	47	48	49
50	51	52	53	54	55	56	57
58	59	60	61	62	63	64	65
66	67	68	69	70	71	72	73
74	75	76	77	78	79	80	81
82	83	84	85	86	87	88	89
90							

Maths Action Plans, Measures, Shape and Space Year 5/P6 © David Clemson and Wendy Clemson, Nelson Thornes Ltd, 2002

Two-digit game cards

Photocopy on card and cut out.

11	12	13	14	15
21	22	23	24	25
31	32	33	34	35
41	42	43	44	45
51	52	53	54	55
61	62	63	64	65
71	72	73	74	75
81	82	83	84	85

16	17	18	19	10
26	27	28	29	20
36	37	38	39	30
46	47	48	49	40
56	57	58	59	50
66	67	68	69	60
76	77	78	79	70
86	87	88	89	80
				90

Maths Action Plans, Measures, Shape and Space Year 5/P6 © David Clemson and Wendy Clemson, Nelson Thornes Ltd, 2002

Symmetry grids (1)

Reflect the shapes into each quarter of the grids.

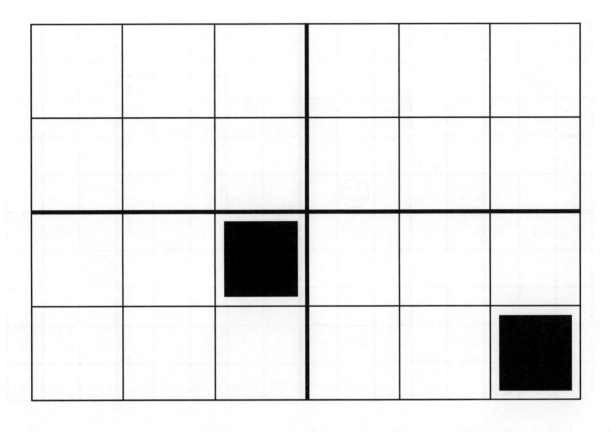

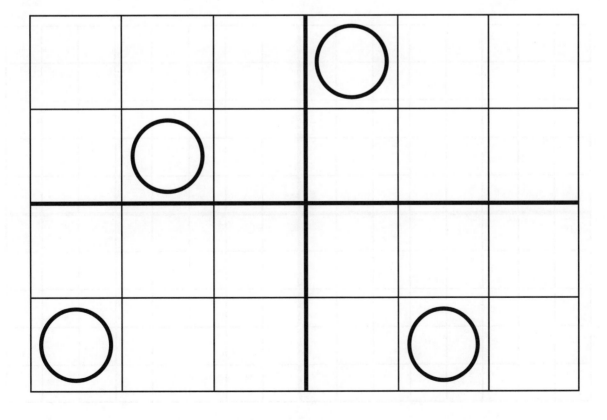

Maths Action Plans, Measures, Shape and Space Year 5/P6 © David Clemson and Wendy Clemson, Nelson Thornes Ltd, 2002

129

Symmetry grids (2)

A Reflect the shapes into each quarter of the grid.

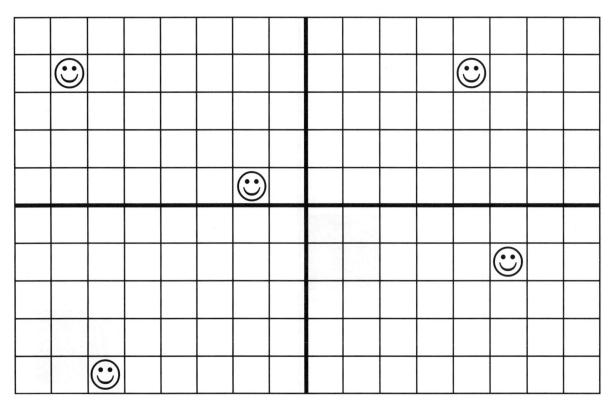

B Draw your own pattern to reflect in each quarter of this grid.

Maths Action Plans, Measures, Shape and Space Year 5/P6 © David Clemson and Wendy Clemson, Nelson Thornes Ltd, 2002

Translated shapes (1)

Draw in the shapes when they have been translated.

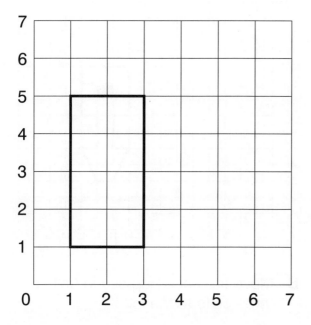

A Move the shape two units to the right.

B Move the shape one unit to the left.

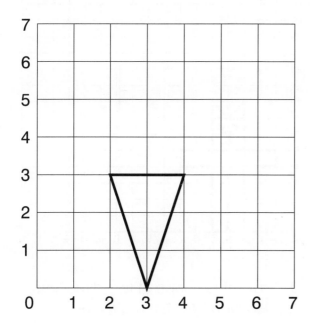

C Move the shape up three units.

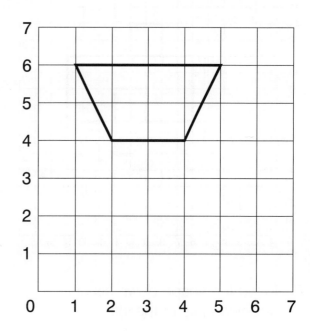

D Move the shape down four units.

Maths Action Plans, Measures, Shape and Space Year 5/P6 © David Clemson and Wendy Clemson, Nelson Thornes Ltd, 2002

Translated shapes (2)

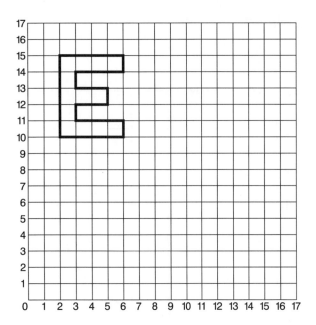

A Move the shape five units to the right and down two units.

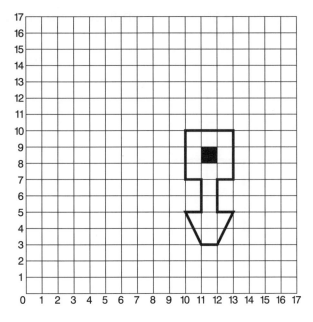

B Move the shape up seven units and three units to the left.

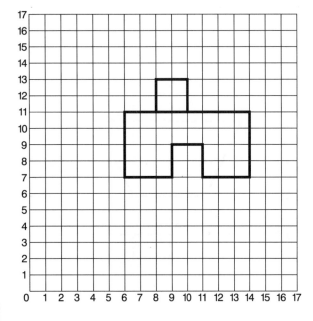

C Move the shape down six units and two units to the left.

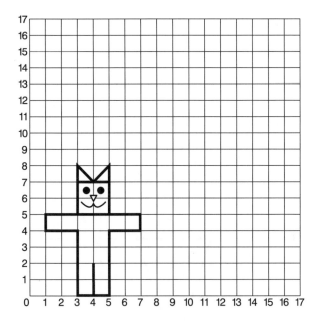

D Move this shape in two directions. Describe how far you moved it:

Maths Action Plans, Measures, Shape and Space Year 5/P6 © David Clemson and Wendy Clemson, Nelson Thornes Ltd, 2002

Diagonals (1)

Draw in the diagonals.

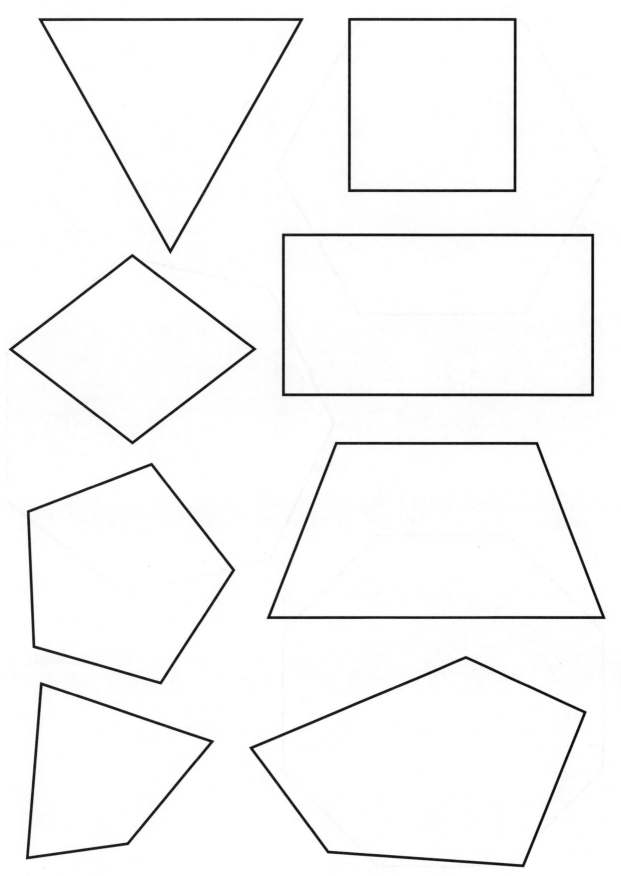

Maths Action Plans, Measures, Shape and Space Year 5/P6 © David Clemson and Wendy Clemson, Nelson Thornes Ltd, 2002

Diagonals (2)

Draw in the diagonals.

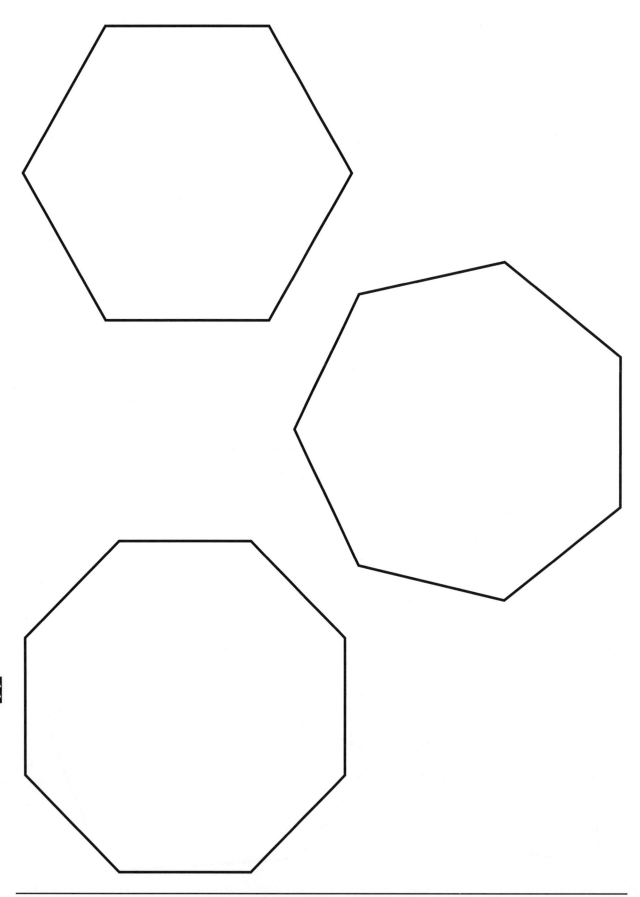

Maths Action Plans, Measures, Shape and Space Year 5/P6 © David Clemson and Wendy Clemson, Nelson Thornes Ltd, 2002

Perimeters (1)

Work out the perimeter of each of these shapes.

Name the shape:

Perimeter:

Name the shape:

Perimeter:

Name the shape:

Perimeter:

Name the shape:

Perimeter:

Name the shape:

Perimeter:

Maths Action Plans, Measures, Shape and Space Year 5/P6 © David Clemson and Wendy Clemson, Nelson Thornes Ltd, 2002

Perimeters (2)

Work out the perimeters.

A An equilateral triangle has a side of 4 cm. What is its perimeter?

B A pentagon has a side of 7 cm. What is its perimeter?

C An octagon has a side of 12 cm. What is its perimeter?

D A square has a side of 6.5 cm. What is its perimeter?

E A hexagon has a side of 5.5 cm. What is its perimeter?

Maths Action Plans, Measures, Shape and Space Year 5/P6 © David Clemson and Wendy Clemson, Nelson Thornes Ltd, 2002

Hairdressing appointments (1)

Melanie		Declan		Jade		Paul	
						8:50	Make coffee
						9:00	Set out equipment
				9:15	Sanjay (dry cut)		
9:30	Carl (dry cut)			9:45	Geraldine (highlights)	9:30– 10:45	Wash Sweep up
		10:00	Sol (cut and colour)				
10:30	Gwen (lowlights)						
		11:15	Pete (cut/blow dry)			11:00– 12:00	Reception Make lunch Wash up
				11:30	Angus and Boris (dry cut – children's)		
		12:00	Sharon (super condition)	12:15	Sheila (cut/blow dry)		
12:30	Sue (cut/blow dry)						
		13:00	Philippa (special occasion)			13:00	Wash as necessary Assist Declan and Jade
				13:45	David (cut/blow dry)		
14:15	Sumi (cut/blow dry)					15:00	Make tea
				15:30	June (perm)		
		15:45	Alisha (cut and colour)				
16:00	Steven (cut/blow dry)					16:00	Sweep floors Wash equipment
		16:55	William (cut/blow dry)				

This is an appointment timetable for a day at a hairdressing salon. The names of the hairdressing team appear at the top of the columns showing their timetables. This is how long the different treatments take:

- dry cut: 20 minutes
- super condition: 50 minutes
- highlights: 1 hour and 45 minutes
- cut and colour: 1 hour and 10 minutes
- special occasion: 2 hours and 45 minutes

- cut/blow dry: 40 minutes
- perm: $2\frac{1}{2}$ hours
- lowlights: 2 hours

Hairdressing appointments (2)

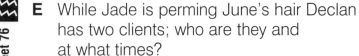

A What is Melanie doing at …

- 10:45?

- 14:50?

- 15:10?

B What is Paul doing at …

- 10:30?

- 11:45?

- 13:30?

- 15:15?

C What is Declan doing when Melanie begins Sue's cut and blow dry?

D What is Jade doing after Angus and Boris's dry cuts?

E While Jade is perming June's hair Declan has two clients; who are they and at what times?

1

2

F Who do you think might have the longest lunch break?

Who will have the shortest?

Railway timetable

Here is a part of a railway timetable. Use it to solve the problems below:

Aberdeen		05:50 e	08:00 e	09:15		
Dundee		07:18 e	09:07 e	10:22		
Edinburgh	06:50	09:10	10:40	11:41		14:40
Haymarket	06:55	09:15	10:45	11:55		14:45
Glasgow Central	08:20		11:20	12:15	12:30	
Motherwell	08:35		11:38		12:44	
Lockerbie	09:22	10:10			13:29	15:41
Carlisle	09:47	10:35	12:05	13:15	13:55	16:07
Penrith	10:03	10:51	12:20		14:11	16:23
Oxenholme Lake District	10:29	11:17	12:46	13:53	14:37	16:49

(e means change at Edinburgh)

A Fill in the answer box to say how long each journey takes:

From	To	Train departs at	How long the journey takes
Edinburgh	Motherwell	06:50	
Dundee	Glasgow Central	09:07	
Glasgow Central	Oxenholme Lake District	12:30	
Lockerbie	Penrith	10:10	

B Mr Finlay is at Glasgow Central. He has missed the 12:15 and wants to travel to Carlisle.

When is the next train?

How long must he wait?

Maths Action Plans, Measures, Shape and Space Year 5/P6 © David Clemson and Wendy Clemson, Nelson Thornes Ltd, 2002

Product and number cards

Photocopy on thin card and cut out.

2	4	6	8	10	12	14	16
18	20	3	9	15	21	24	27
30	28	32	36	40	5	25	35
45	50	42	48	54	60	49	56
63	70	64	72	80	81	90	7
100							

2	3	4	5
6	7	8	9
10			

Maths Action Plans, Measures, Shape and Space Year 5/P6 © David Clemson and Wendy Clemson, Nelson Thornes Ltd, 2002

Estimate times

A Suggest happenings that you would estimate in …

• weeks:

• months:

• years:

• decades:

• centuries:

B Would we choose to measure these in seconds, minutes, hours, days, weeks, months or years?

The time it takes for a runner bean to grow:

The time it takes to brush our hair:

The time it takes to key in a telephone number:

The time it takes to get a night's sleep:

C How would you measure these?
How much older or younger than your friend you are:

How long it takes to run a cross-country race:

How much time?

Make estimates and then work these out using a calculator.
Write down how you worked them out.

A How many minutes in a day?   Estimate: [ ]   Answer: [ ]

How I worked it out:

B How many hours in a week?   Estimate: [ ]   Answer: [ ]

How I worked it out:

C How many days since you were born?   Estimate: [ ]   Answer: [ ]

How I worked it out:

D How many minutes sleep have you had in the last week?   Estimate: [ ]   Answer: [ ]

How I worked it out:

E How many seconds did you spend eating yesterday?   Estimate: [ ]   Answer: [ ]

How I worked it out:

Maths Action Plans, Measures, Shape and Space Year 5/P6 © David Clemson and Wendy Clemson, Nelson Thornes Ltd, 2002

Measuring capacity

A Measure the capacity of the containers exactly, using a measuring jug or cylinder.
Record your answers.

Container	Capacity

B Convert these into ml:

45 l [ ]   100 l [ ]

4.5 l [ ]   1000 l [ ]

3 l [ ]   10 l [ ]

10 l [ ]   72 l [ ]

C Convert these into pints:

1 gallon [ ]   25% gallon [ ]

10 gallons [ ]   13 gallons [ ]

½ gallon [ ]   ¾ gallon [ ]

Maths Action Plans, Measures, Shape and Space Year 5/P6 © David Clemson and Wendy Clemson, Nelson Thornes Ltd, 2002

Resource sheet 81

Match capacities

A Join up those which match:

3 000 ml

1 pint

1 litre

5.5 litres

1 gallon

250 ml

About 1¾ pints

¼ litre

5 500 millilitres

Slightly less than 5 litres

3 litres exactly

570 ml approx.

B Write in a new matching capacity for each of these and join them up:

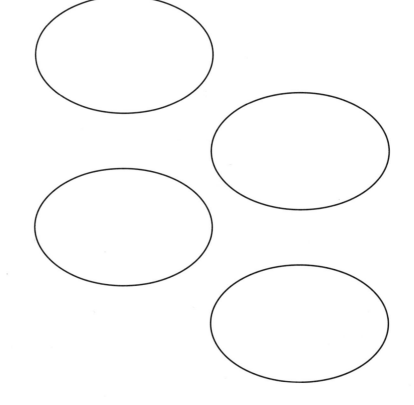

1 litre

1 pint

1 gallon

1 millilitre

Maths Action Plans, Measures, Shape and Space Year 5/P6 © David Clemson and Wendy Clemson, Nelson Thornes Ltd, 2002

Check the timetable

Here is a part of a railway timetable. Use it to solve the problems below:

Aberdeen		05:50 e	08:00 e	09:15		
Dundee		07:18 e	09:07 e	10:22		
Edinburgh	06:50	09:10	10:40	11:41		14:40
Haymarket	06:55	09:15	10:45	11:55		14:45
Glasgow Central	08:20		11:20	12:15	12:30	
Motherwell	08:35		11:38		12:44	
Lockerbie	09:22	10:10			13:29	15:41
Carlisle	09:47	10:35	12:05	13:15	13:55	16:07
Penrith	10:03	10:51	12:20		14:11	16:23
Oxenholme Lake District	10:29	11:17	12:46	13:53	14:37	16:49

(e means change at Edinburgh)

A At what time do trains depart from Penrith?

B When is the next train after …

• the 11:38 from Motherwell?

• the 10:45 from Haymarket?

• the 09:07 from Dundee?

C Where is the 10:40 from Edinburgh at these times?

10:45

11:00

12:05

12:15

Maths Action Plans, Measures, Shape and Space Year 5/P6 © David Clemson and Wendy Clemson, Nelson Thornes Ltd, 2002

Make some estimates

A How long is it …

- until your birthday?

- until Christmas?

B How much time …

- do you spend in school each week?

- do you spend watching sport on TV each week?

- do you spend on the telephone each day?

- is there between 08:00 on 2 June and 08:00 on 14 June?

- is there between one full moon and the next?

C Choose two of the happenings above, that you think you could measure.
Write down in detail how you would measure them.

Maths Action Plans, Measures, Shape and Space Year 5/P6 © David Clemson and Wendy Clemson, Nelson Thornes Ltd, 2002

Tide table

Here is part of a tide timetable for the Irish Sea.

October	High water Morning	High water Afternoon	Low water Morning	Low water Afternoon
7 Sun	01:32	13:45	8:13	20:30
8 Mon	02:06	14:21	08:47	21:06
9 Tue	02:28	15:08	09:25	21:54
10 Wed	03:46	16:15	10:17	23:04
11 Thu	05:07	17:47	11:40	
12 Fri	06:37	19:12	00:47	13:19
13 Sat	07:57	20:23	02:09	14:33
14 Sun	09:01	21:20	03:15	15:33
15 Mon	09:51	22:10	04:12	16:25
16 Tue	10:38	22:56	05:02	17:13
17 Wed	11:21	23:40	05:48	17:58
18 Thu		12:02	06:30	18:40
19 Fri	00:20	12:43	07:10	19:22
20 Sat	01:01	13:21	07:48	20:33

A How long is it from morning high water to afternoon high water on:

8 October? _____

14 October? _____

19 October? _____

B Why is there no time for morning high water on 18 October?

_____

Dotty paper squares

Maths Action Plans, Measures, Shape and Space Year 5/P6 © David Clemson and Wendy Clemson, Nelson Thornes Ltd, 2002

Squared paper (1 cm)

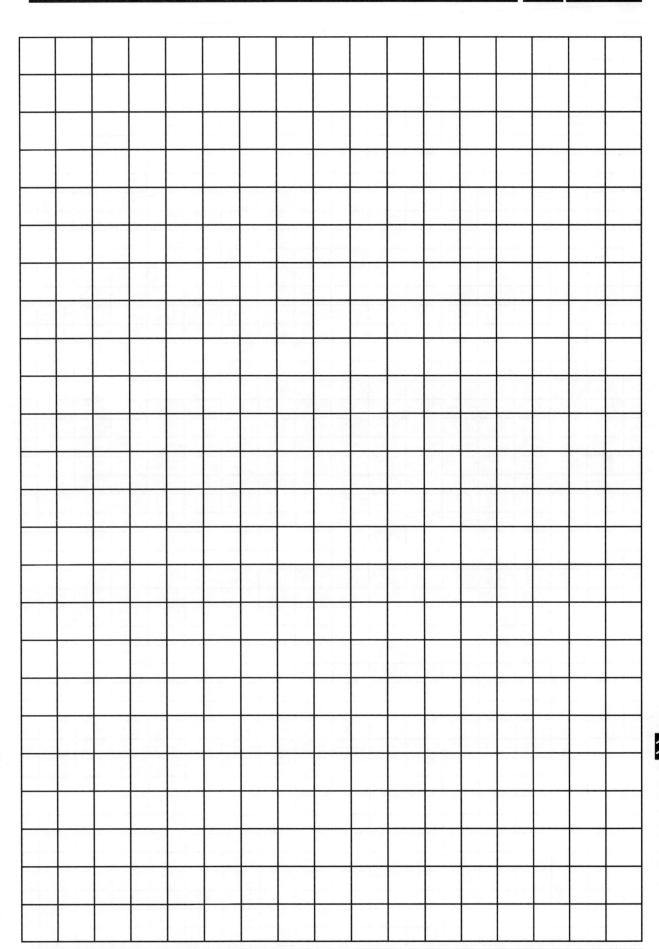

Maths Action Plans, Measures, Shape and Space Year 5/P6 © David Clemson and Wendy Clemson, Nelson Thornes Ltd, 2002

General resource sheet B

Squared paper (½ cm)

GENERAL RESOURCE SHEET C

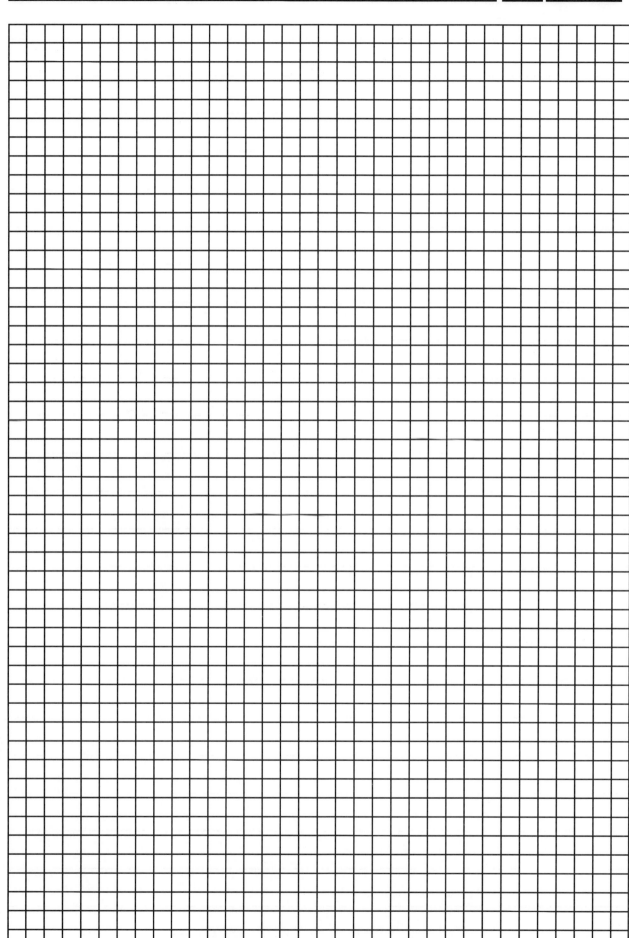

Symmetry grid

 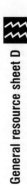

Maths Action Plans, Measures, Shape and Space Year 5/P6 © David Clemson and Wendy Clemson, Nelson Thornes Ltd, 2002

Game cards

Maths Action Plans, Measures, Shape and Space Year 5/P6 © David Clemson and Wendy Clemson, Nelson Thornes Ltd, 2002